KAROO

Katryn v/Heerden 1993

KAROO

South African Wild Flower Guide 6

Text by
DAVID SHEARING

Illustrations by
KATRYN VAN HEERDEN

This guide is the sixth in a series of Flower Guides published by the Botanical Society of S.A. in association with National Botanical Institute 1994

The Botanical Society of South Africa was founded in 1913 to support the National Botanic Gardens, to promote the conservation and cultivation of our indigenous flora and to provide environmental education

One of our projects is the publication of a series of wild flower guides.
Published to date are::

Guide 1: Namaqualand & Clanwilliam (1st edition)	1981
Guide 1: (revised) Namaqualand	1988/1996/1997
Guide 2: Outeniqua	
Tsitsikamma & Eastern Little Karoo	1982/1997
Guide 3: Cape Peninsula	1983/1996
Guide 4: Transvaal Lowveld & Escarpment	1984
Guide 5: Hottentots Holland to Hermanus	1985
Guide 6: Karoo	1994/1997
Guide 7: West Coast	1996
Guide 8: Southern Overberg	1997

These and future guides will eventually cover most of the wild flowers of South Africa.

First edition. First impression 1994
Second impression 1997
Botanical Society of South Africa
Kirstenbosch, Claremont 7735 RSA

Copyright © Text & paintings
Botanical Society of South Africa

Edited by Annelise le Roux
Design and production by Wim Reinders & Associates, Cape Town
Typeset by 4-Ways DTP Services, Cape Town
Reproduction by Hirt &Carter, Cape Town
Printed by National Book Printers, Drukkery Street, Goodwood, Western Cape

ISBN 1-874999-04-X

FOREWORD

It is now some fifteen years since the Council of the Botanical Society decided that the time was long overdue for the production of a series of botanical field guides to introduce the citizens of South Africa to the wonderful floral heritage of their country. Funds were found to launch an authoritative series of inexpensive illustrated field guides which, while botanically accurate and informative, could nevertheless be used easily by the interested naturalist to acquaint him/herself with the major flora of a region. So far six of these popular guides have been produced in English and Afrikaans each covering geographically interesting regions of South Africa, and over 60 000 copies have reached the hands of wild flower enthusiasts throughout the land.

This book is the latest in the Society's series of botanical field guides and covers by far the largest area of any of the series: the "ver verlate vlaktes" of the Great and Little Karoo of South Africa. It differs somewhat from its predecessors in that it is designed specifically for the farmers of the region and carries an abundance of agricultural information which the Society hopes the farming community will find useful. Much of the text represents a distillation of the author, David Shearing's, many years of practical experience as a farmer in the Karoo, and the reported grazing value of every species represented in this book has been thoroughly established by him. Each of the 400 odd species has been carefully selected because of its representation and relative importance in the plant community of its area. The Society also hopes that this guide, with its wealth of taxonomic and agroscientific detail will prove a useful addition to the field libraries of the students attending the renowned agricultural colleges of the region.

Our artist, Katryn van Heerden, has not only portrayed each specimen with superb botanical accuracy, but has been able to capture with great delicacy the floral character of each of her subjects. As a self-taught wild flower painter encouraged by that doyenne of floral artists, Fay Anderson, Katryn has truly brought to life the remarkable flora of the region of her birth.

I feel sure that this book will prove its worth as an invaluable conservation tool and wish the user, be he/she farmer, scientist, student or naturalist, many happy hours of botanizing in the Karoo with this guide as companion.

Professor O.A.M. Lewis
President, Botanical Society of South Africa

Katryn v Heerden 1991

Katryn v. Heerden
1989

CONTENTS

Katryn vHeerden 19

ACKNOWLEDGEMENTS

Many people have helped me in preparing this guide. Without them I would have been lost.

Most of all I would like to express my deepest appreciation to Katryn van Heerden who illustrated this book. She works full time, and sometimes, in her lunch hour, would have to 'catch' a flower that closed at night. Other specimens kept her busy till the early hours of the morning, using shades and hues I never even saw. She has completed a great task with skill and good humour, and for this I thank her.

Annelise le Roux helped plan the guide, and worked hard to give it as much advertisement as possible. She was responsible for editing it as well as for the Afrikaans translation with the help of Anneke de Kock and always seemed to be at the receiving end of the telephone when I wanted advice. Together with Bruce Bayer and Brand van Breda she gave me invaluable help with distributions and habitats.

Harold Braack has a special claim on me. While he was Park Warden of the Karoo National Park he spent time persuading me to write this book. My thanks to him and his wife Toni for their continual encouragement.

Naming the plants is always a problem. My thanks to the old BRI and their successors the NBI in Pretoria, Kirstenbosch, Grahamstown and last but very definitely not least, Stellenbosch, who checked the names of every single specimen in a very short time. Also to Prof. Roy Lubke of Rhodes University and Dawie Blom of Grootfontein College of Agriculture for helping with this work. And finally all those botanists, mostly unknown, all over the world who checked the final identifications for me.

Bridget Randall, a qualified botanist, was stationed at the Karoo National Park for some time. She helped with the identification and collection of many specimens painted while she was here.

Pat Marincowitz, Apie Wiid, Eddie Bezuidenhout, Sue Dean, Bruce Bayer and Dawie Blom have all helped with the common names and some interesting stories connected with these plants. Kiewiet Danster told me of the beliefs of his San forebears and how they used the plants medicinally.

Dr Piet Roux, formerly Director of the Karoo Region, and Andy Gubb, formerly of the Macgregor Museum in Kimberley, both helped with ideas and advice.

A special word of thanks is due to the National Parks Board for all their help and hard work. They very kindly allowed me to collect plants in the Karoo National Park and also helped in many other smaller ways.

The Staff of the Beaufort West Provincial Library have been very patient and helpful in lending the text books I required for research.

Dr John Rourke and the Botanical Society for believing in this guide, helping me over the many difficulties and making urgent identifications.

To my wife Taffy, many thanks for putting up with all those thorny plants scratching you while on their way to Beaufort West to be painted, and for all your help and support when it was most needed. A special word of thanks for checking my manuscript and pointing out how it could be improved.

To all those others who have helped me with advice, ideas, stories and any other fact, my grateful thanks. This guide would not have been possible had it not been for your help.

ACKNOWLEDGEMENTS FOR THE SECOND EDITION

The interest displayed in the first edition of this handbook has necessitated an early reprint. This has given me the chance to make the few corrections necessary and also to update the botanical names where they have changed.

I want to thank Mr John Kirsten, Assistant-Director of the Karoo Region of the Northern Cape Province's Department of Agriculture for looking through the original text and suggesting a few changes.

The staff of the Compton Herbarium, Kirstenbosch, were responsible for the updating of the botanical names. My thanks are extended to them as well as to the Botanical Society for their continued interest in this book.

DAVID SHEARING

These guides are made possible through the co-operation of members of both the public and private sector through their dedication to the conservation of our floral wealth. The Publications Committee that has motivated the series consist of the following bodies: the Cape Nature Conservation, the National Botanical Institute, the Bolus Herbarium of the University of Cape Town and the Botanical Society of South Africa.

THE KAROO REGION

Introduction

The Karoo, that vast arid plain occupying most of the interior of the Cape Province, is astoundingly rich in flora. It has been estimated that over 7 000 different species occur in this area – more than three times as many as in the British Isles.

The flora found in the Karoo today is very different from that seen by the first White settlers that moved their flocks here from the coastal regions. In those early days there were no fences and no windmills. The only domestic animals were those owned by the Khoisan tribes. These moved along with the tribe or family from water hole to water hole, and were far fewer in number than those grazed in the Karoo today.

There were, of course, millions of antelope – mainly springbuck – and numerous larger animals scattered throughout the countryside. We do not have estimates of the number of animals that grazed here, but it has been calculated that the population of wild animals in the United States of America when the European first arrived there, was two and a half times as great as their present population of domestic livestock. There is no reason to suppose that the proportions in the two countries would differ very much. Despite all this, no, or very little, overgrazing took place. This could be because different species of animals graze a different selection of plants, and under the migratory system the veld had long rest periods.

If you stand on the banks of a Karoo river today, it is difficult to imagine that only a couple of centuries ago there were animals like hippopotamus grazing there whose daily intake of feed could be measured in hundreds of kilograms. Petroglyphs left by the San also indicate that elephant and rhino once roamed the Karoo plains.

The difference in the circumstances becomes obvious with study. Before the countryside was divided into farms and settled, there were a great variety of wild animals roaming freely. Not being confined, they were able to graze heavily and then move on, giving the plants a chance to recover. They were also dependant on surface water and when this dried up they moved on or died. Today we have made it possible for the animals to remain on the veld, regardless of conditions, by pumping water from underground. This can damage the veld very considerably when animals trample bushes that have become brittle under drought conditions.

The flora of the Karoo has over the centuries adapted to this drought-prone environment. Many of the plants are able to withstand long periods with little or no water, as well as variations in temperature, from heavy frost in the winter to over 50 °C in the summer.

The flora of the Karoo is the economy of the area. The only way farmers can make a living is by grazing their animals on the veld. The rainfall is too low for any artificial pastures, except where there is strong underground water or large storage dams. This means that the flora of this area is of prime economic importance to those that farm here and must be conserved at all costs as it cannot be replaced by anything else. In fact the Karoo farmer farms his bushes and uses the sheep and goats as harvesters.

History

The 'Wildschietboeken', or permits issued to the first European farmers in the country, are in the Cape Archives. These farmers were known as 'trek-boere', for the very good reason that they never stayed on one farm for any number of years, but 'trekked' (moved) to another as soon as the old farm was 'farmed out'. These permits entitled the farmer to graze his animals and to hunt on the specified farm for a period of one year for the sum of 12 rix dollars, or in today's terms, R1,80. In quite a few cases this was too high, and the farmer would move on because he couldn't pay.

But the main reason for moving on was that the farm was 'finished'. The average farm was about 6 000 ha, and the farmer would have hundreds of cattle and thousands of sheep, besides the horses and other stock which he hardly considered worth mentioning. Add to this the vast numbers of wild animals that used to roam the Karoo plains at that time, and it is hardly surprising that the grazing did not last.

We do not know exactly what the Karoo looked like when these settlers arrived. It has been postulated that there was very much more grass then than there is now. This is borne out by the grass pollen deposited at that time. Others disagree and say there are years, even now, when the Karoo is a sea of grass, but that it could never be considered grassland. What is certain, though, is that the grazing was far better then than it is now.

Grazing pressures today vary from 1 sheep on 2,5 to 10 ha, depending on the veld. In 1936 an official of the Department of Agriculture wrote that the carrying capacity of the Karoo varied from 1 sheep to 0,8 ha to 1 sheep to 2,5 ha 'in the very worst veld'. In about the year 1800 there would have been many farms where the stocking rate would have been in excess of 4,5 sheep to the ha. This is about 12 times today's rate.

What happens when veld is overgrazed? The animals eat the most palatable plants first, and they then keep them grazed right down so that they have no chance of producing seed. Over a period of years these plants diminish in numbers, and eventually even disappear. If these practices continue, the veld deteriorates in species composition and cover to the extent where the grazing capacity is drastically affected.

Luckily the seed of Karoo bushes have a very long life. They can remain dormant in the seedbed for up to 70 years, and then still germinate. However, the deterioration of the veld that takes place in a few short years takes many times that period of time to return to an optimum condition. Contrary to general belief, drought does not adversely affect Karoo veld. Indeed it has been shown that superior veld comes through a drought in an improved condition, though inferior veld does deteriorate further.

What does happen to inferior veld is that a huge amount of the topsoil is lost through erosion. If there are no bushes and grasses to slow the water and wind down, the soil is eroded away by both donga and sheet erosion. This is possibly the most important factor in overgrazing. If there is no soil, there can be very few plants. And then, if there are few or no plants, the erosion is aggravated, and even the seed that does set erodes away with the soil.

Area

The area covered by this book is that generally known as Karoo – reaching from the Orange River to Oudtshoorn and, from the west coast to Somerset East. The Karoo is easily divided into a winter rainfall region including Namaqualand, Tanqua Karoo and the Little Karoo, and the summer rainfall region comprising Bushmanland, Northern, Upper and Great Karoo and the mountains of the Great Escarpment. The mountains of the Cape Fold Belt between the Great Karoo and Little Karoo have a higher rainfall and therefore the vegetation is very different. This fynbos vegetation is not only floristically different from the Karoo vegetation, but also structurally with a higher percentage plant cover, higher shrubs and less succulency.

The area mainly covered by the illustrations, however, is that bordered by the Swartberg mountains from Laingsburg to Willowmore in the south; northwards through Graaff-Reinet to a line running through Hanover, Britstown and Vanwyksvlei, and then coming down the west from Brandvlei to between Calvinia and Williston to Sutherland and back to Laingsburg. Most of the specimens used in the accompanying paintings were collected in the area between Fraserburg and Nelspoort, which lies almost in the centre of the Karoo. These plants will occur in the outlying districts to a lesser degree, but will nevertheless still be found. On the other hand, plants from those areas will be found near Beaufort West, though possibly in smaller numbers.

In the very centre of this area lies the Karoo National Park. This Park's main tourist attraction is its rugged scenery and its flora. Almost all plants shown in this guide occur in the Park, and, indeed, many were collected there.

Rainfall

The annual average precipitation of the summer rainfall region decreases westwards from about 450 mm in the east to about 150 mm in the west. The number of rainy days also decreases in the same way. Most of this rain is, on average, summer rain, with the northern and western parts being most prone to droughts.

A drought is when rainfall is 60% of average or less. The Karoo is subject to such droughts for between 30% and 50% of the time, which is more than for other parts of our country. This means these droughts are the rule, with good years being the exception, and plants have acclimatized themselves to these circumstances to a great degree.

Soil erosion

Soil erosion in the Karoo varies from moderate to severe. The symptoms can either be conspicuous, as in the case of donga erosion, or inconspicuous, as in sheet erosion. Both are, however, equally serious. The natural erosion that has taken place since time began is not a factor to worry about. Man-made erosion on the other hand is a far more serious problem to the continued existence of the Karoo as we know it. It is this kind of erosion that is associated with the desertification process.

Man-made erosion is usually the result of incorrect treatment, and use of land for purposes for which it is not suited. Smallstock farming in confined areas is an example of such incorrect usage, and it must be practiced with the utmost care to prevent large-scale erosion.

Overgrazing by domestic animals is the main cause of man-made erosion. In 1930 sheep numbers in South Africa peaked at about 48 million. In 1986 it was estimated that the Karoo Region could safely carry about 7 to 7,5 million small stock units. However, in that year there were about 10 million small stock units in this region, giving an overstocking rate of almost 30%.

Consequently the single largest reason for the degeneration of the plant cover and the resultant erosion, is too many animals per farming unit.

Grazing practices

Often though the farmer has great difficulty in learning about the plants on his farm. As stated, there is a huge variety, and this on its own is daunting to most. Because he then does not know his plants well enough, he cannot recognise the early signs of overgrazing. In bad cases he may only recognise it when it is far advanced and bare patches are visible. More commonly the slow replacement of good grazing bushes by less palatable ones is not obvious to anyone who does not know and understand his veld. For too long now veld, in some farmers' eyes, has just been veld, and is there solely for their animals to graze. Sadly little or no thought has been given to what happens if the balance is upset and some varieties diminish in numbers to the extent that they may as well be extinct.

Because there are very few available 'farmer friendly' books I have attempted to highlight grazing values of the plants in this guide. A problem has been that the value of a plant in Graaff-Reinet need not be the same as it will be for the identical plant in Calvinia. This is discussed in the section on palatability.

This problem is to some extent alleviated by 'plant rallies', plant identification days and, for those near the Karoo National Park, the 'bossie trails' and plant identifications at the agricultural shows.

We should also remember that conservation and making money do not always walk hand in hand. There are times in many a farmer's life when he finds he must look into his Bank Manager's eyes rather than his veld's. Input costs are very high today, and like everyone else, the farmer must pay for what he receives. This does not always coincide with the long-term view that conservation pays. It remains true that the farmer who takes no note of the conservation status of his veld, is doomed to see it regress, to his eventual detriment.

But conservation practices are almost the norm today. Flocks and herds of unproductive animals are very seldom encountered today. Farmers find it pays them to keep fewer highly productive animals than large numbers whose production ability is questionable. Another hopeful sign is the way donga beds are now so often covered in plant growth. There are many older farmers who maintain that the veld condition today is better than it was in the 40's and 50's. I would like to think they are correct.

The grazing practices advocated today are vastly different from those of a few decades ago. It was undoubtedly uncontrolled and indiscriminate grazing that reduced the Karoo to its semi-desert state. It is a supreme challenge to reverse this trend, and one that the whole country must meet.

One side effect of bad grazing practices over the past decades is the fact that good grazing land in the Karoo is becoming infested with shrubs that, for all intents and purposes, are almost worthless to the farmer. *Rhigozum trichotomum* (**driedoring**) has increased to the extent that it now occurs over 9,5 million ha, while *Lycium* species (**kriedoring**) occur in varying degrees of intensity over 10,9 million ha. Invaders like *Prosopis* species (**mesquite**) have already occupied 200 000 ha and are still spreading fast. Besides these there are now dense stands of *Elytropappus rhinocerotis* (**rhinoceros bush**) and *Euryops* species (**resin bush**) where before they were almost absent.

A number of different grazing methods have been used over the years. Originally the farmers didn't have camps or even fenced farms, so there was no method applied other than continuous grazing. Some farmers, even after their farms had been fenced, continued this practice although it was proved to be detrimental to the flora because the animals then grazed the most palatable plants before those that were not so palatable. They almost exterminated many species in this way.

The late John Acocks advocated a form of short duration grazing in which large flocks would graze in small camps. Some farmers had notable success with this system, but a major drawback was the cost of providing the camps. Flowing from Acocks' ideas, came the other short duration grazing system, the so-called 'wagon wheel' system. Here the farm was divided into cells, with each cell having camps radiating from the watering point like the spokes of a wheel. Once again the cost of the fencing was a problem, but added to this was the fact that the veld never really had a good long rest.

The Department of Agriculture too has advocated a number of systems over the years. There have been the two-camp system, the three-camp system and now the multi-camp system. All of them call for periods of grazing and periods of resting, and this basic principle seems to give the best results.

In practice many farmers seem to find that they get best results from following their own systems. They argue that no two farms are alike, and, indeed, no two camps on any farm are alike. It is usually felt that each farm needs to be handled on its own merits and that the farmer is best qualified to work out a system for his own farm. There is merit in this as well, provided the farmer knows what he is about. Where, however, his system does not provide the desired results, he is advised to follow one of the Departmental systems which have proved successful in reclaiming the veld.

Personally I base my system on watching what I call my 'positive indicators' rather than the 'negative indicators'. The negative indicators are those plants like *Chrysocoma ciliata* (**bitterbos**) and others that indicate overgrazing. The problem with them is that they can still be present in the veld in large numbers even when that veld has recovered from a previous owner's mismanagement. I find that by watching the most palatable plants, *Limeum aethiopicum* (**koggelmandervoetkaroo**), *Osteospermum sinuatum* (**bietou**) and others, I can decide quickly when a camp has been grazed sufficiently.

Whatever system is used, whether it be a Departmental one or one the farmer has devised, the present day grazing norms must be adhered to. These norms have been worked out according to an animal's mass and the amount of feed it will consume. Each area of the country has been allocated a grazing density in large stock units (usually regarded to be equal to one small ox), and this density must not be exceeded.

Grazing habits
Different animals have different grazing habits. Horses, donkeys and mules concentrate mainly on that level of vegetation between 2 and 12 cm from the surface. Cattle, on the other hand, prefer veld at between 8 and 70 cm, though they are able to use feed up to a height of 1,7 m. Cattle are also mainly grass eaters. Sheep feed at from 2 to 40 cm, but are not as severe on the veld as horses and donkeys. They concentrate on grasses during the summer months and bushes during the winter. Goats are browsers, but under pressure will eat almost anything. They browse comfortably at between 2 and 150 cm, and start at the top and work their way down. They are less selective than sheep, but under pressure can be more severe on the veld.

'Bossie' trails
I helped establish a 'Bossie Trail' in the Karoo National Park, and have laid out some others – on the farms Travalia at Three Sisters, Hartebeesfontein at Nelspoort and Rooiheuwel on the Beaufort West-Fraserburg boundary. A number of plants were marked and identified, and these markers will be regularly updated as the old plants die or become unidentifiable. Almost all these plants are to be found in this guide, and I am sure they will prove useful adjuncts to those who wish to learn to identify the plants of the region.

Karoo National Park

The Karoo National Park, which was officially opened during September 1979, is situated at almost the centre of the area covered by this guide. Consequently, almost all the plants illustrated are to be found within the boundaries of the Park.

The Park was established to preserve the flora and fauna of the area. Because of its aridity, there are not as many animals, particularly large ones, in the Park compared to parks like Kruger National Park. However, the flora is unique, and is considered to be the main attraction.

National Parks Board policy has been to withdraw their veld from grazing till it had recovered to a substantial degree. The result may be seen in parts of the Park – particularly in the mountains where improvement has been most marked.

The Karoo National Park also has some very interesting and scenic walks and trails. Most popular of these is the Springbok Hiking Trail which takes three days to complete. It takes in aspects of the flats, middle plateau and mountain, so a good cross-section of the flora of the Park is to be seen here.

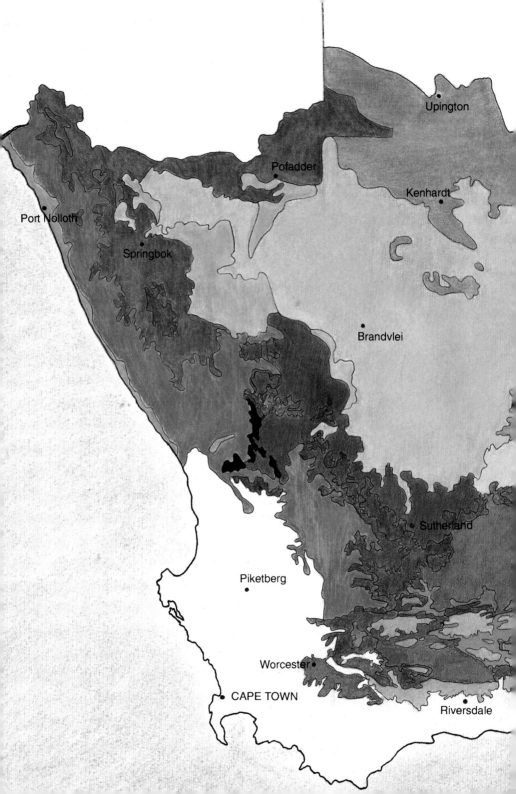

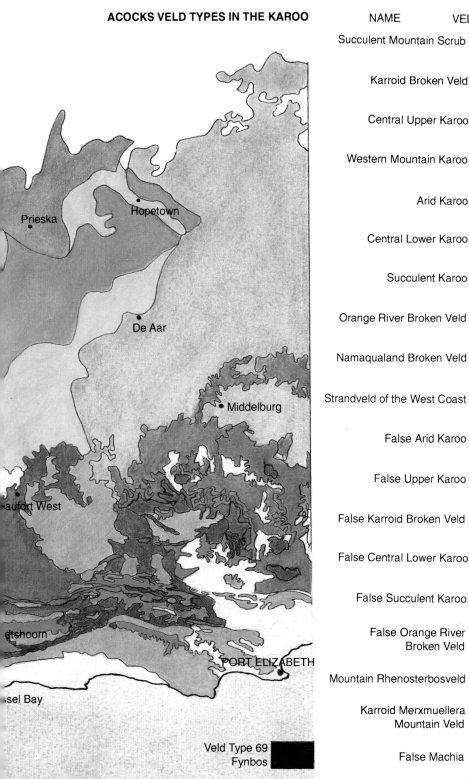

ACOCKS VELD TYPES IN THE KAROO

NAME	VELD TYPE
Succulent Mountain Scrub	25
Karroid Broken Veld	26
Central Upper Karoo	27
Western Mountain Karoo	28
Arid Karoo	29
Central Lower Karoo	30
Succulent Karoo	31
Orange River Broken Veld	32
Namaqualand Broken Veld	33
Strandveld of the West Coast	34
False Arid Karoo	35
False Upper Karoo	36
False Karroid Broken Veld	37
False Central Lower Karoo	38
False Succulent Karoo	39
False Orange River Broken Veld	40
Mountain Rhenosterbosveld	43
Karroid Merxmuellera Mountain Veld	60
False Machia	70

Prieska · Hopetown · De Aar · Middelburg · aufort West · dtshoorn · PORT ELIZABETH · sel Bay

Veld Type 69 Fynbos

ABOUT THE PLANTS

Selection and painting of plants

Plants were selected on the basis that any that are of economic value to the farmer – be it a 5-star or a 1-star plant – must be included. Then any other plant that catches the eye and would be of interest to the visitor is also included. Here it must be remembered that some plants that have no practical grazing value on their own, do have a value in rating the condition of the veld.

These plants have been arranged in the order used by the National Botanical Institute in their handbook *'Plants of southern Africa: names and distribution'*.

All plants in this guide except one page of aloes and related plants, have been painted life-size. Even so it should be remembered that leaf and flower sizes, as well as the total size of the plant, are greatly affected by, for instance, soil, availability of water, wind, heat and a great number of other factors.

Names

The botanical names given were correct when printed. They do, however, change fairly frequently, and no guarantee is given that any plant's name will be the same at a later date. Synonyms are given between brackets on the following line if these have become well-known over the years. Others may be obtained by referring to: Arnold, T.H. & De Wet, B.C. 1993. *Plants of southern Africa: names and distributions*. Memoirs of the Botanical Survey of South Africa No. 62.

Common names have been given where they are known. The more commonly used English and Afrikaans names were chosen. However, not all plants have common names, and those that do, very often have only an Afrikaans one.

Some plants have a great number of common names which vary from region to region. Preference was given to names used by the people of the Great Karoo, the one used most commonly and the one which is likely to cause the least confusion.

The first systematic record of common names was probably made by the gardener, Hendrik Oldenland, during Simon van der Stel's period as Governor. Most Karoo plants were named during the 1700's as this area was not settled to any degree by the White man before then. But it was the Khoi and the San that passed on to the early settlers the vast lore of the plants, and thereby made a very significant contribution to their naming.

Palatability

Farmers are apt to divide their plants into 'good' and 'bad' bushes for grazing purposes. Botanically and ecologically speaking, there is no such thing as either a 'good' bush or a 'bad' one. They all belong to the plant community, and are there for a reason. The so-called 'bad' plants are often pioneer forms. These are usually more highly specialized than those climax or 'good' bushes. Being pioneers they have evolved many intricate adaptations to stress, tolerance and survival. One of these adaptations is that their seed can often remain viable in the seedbed for longer periods than can those of the climax species.

During normal stress situations such as drought, fire and heavy utilization, the veld must go through the natural process of pioneer to climax plants. The better the condition of the veld prior to the stress, the more rapid the return of the climax plants. This is not because of the presence of 'good' seed – they are all present at all times – but because environmental parameters such as soil fertility, moisture, cover, nutrients, etc. return more rapidly to the community.

Plants vary in their palatability from area to area. Assessing a value for this palatability, has been based on conditions in the Beaufort West/Fraserburg area. Even in this area some plants vary greatly according to the aspect on which they grow, or some other condition.

Roughly speaking, palatability may be described as the characteristic of a plant that stimulates an animal to eat it. This, in turn appears to be bound up with the amount of ether extract found in the plant as well as its outward appearance. If it has many thorns or spines, is woody or has hairs on leaves and/or stems, it is not so palatable. Animals do not appear to graze hairy plants easily. This is therefore probably one of nature's safeguards – particularly where the young plant is covered with hairs. See page 31 for grazing values.

The selection of a certain species depends largely on what other plants are growing in that area. The number of plants of that species also plays a part as animals do not like to graze only one kind.

Flowering times

Most Karoo plants' flowering times are coupled to the rainfall, therefore with very few exceptions, it is not possible to give exact times of flowering. However, it may be assumed that the main flowering period will be spring to early summer and again in autumn – if sufficient rain has fallen.

Some plants seem to break all rules. **Wild pomegranate** (*Rhigozum obovatum*) for instance, does not necessarily flower even when enough rain has fallen. On the other hand, unless it is really very dry, some flowers can usually be found, especially in spring.

Exotic plants

Many plants have been introduced from, mainly, Europe and the Americas. They have in many cases become naturalized, and not many people realize that they do not belong to the Karoo flora. Some of these plants, indeed, are very important economically. *Atriplex semibacata* (**creeping saltbush**) is an excellent grazing plant, while *Cuscuta campestris* (**dodder**) can ruin a crop of lucerne if not kept in check.

Many exotic plants have been included, and the word 'exotic' has been used to make them easily identifiable.

Medicinal plants

In days gone by the farmers in this area had no chemist to turn to for their medicines, so they used the local bushes. Much of this knowledge has disappeared, but where I have managed to find a record, it has been included in the text. Much knowledge was lost because people were never supposed to speak about the medicines they were given. In this way they didn't give a remedy a bad name if it didn't work!

It must be emphasized that herbal remedies can also be dangerous. They should not be used indiscriminately or without adequate care. Nor should they be given in huge doses to try and make them act faster. Plants are also listed as having been used, for instance, to 'cure' cancer. This is done for the sake of completeness, and not because it necessarily worked. No guarantee is given or implied that any of these remedies will work, and anyone wishing to try one of them should consult a doctor or herbalist first.

Poisonous plants

There are a great many plants occurring in the Great Karoo that contain poisonous substances. Luckily many of these taste so bad that they are seldom eaten by humans. Stock losses in South Africa of up to 25% can on the other hand be directly ascribed to plant poisoning, so cognisance must be taken of them. This is also not the end of the story. For each animal that dies of poisoning, there may be a couple that recover but whose production is affected as a result of the poison. It has been estimated that the financial loss from these sick animals may be twice that of the dead ones.

The better the condition of the veld, the less likely it is that animals will eat poisonous plants. It can therefore be argued that many deaths have been caused directly by overgrazing. Overgrazing certainly enables invader plants to increase. Some of these invader plants are poisonous, *viz.* **bitterbos** (*Chrysocoma ciliata*), *Senecio* species, *Moraea* species, *Homeria* species, **dubbeltjie** (*Tribulus terrestris*), **vermeerbos** (*Geigeria* species) and **slangkop** (*Ornithoglossum* species).

As far as people are concerned, it is safer not to eat berries and/or leaves unless you know which are poisonous. Some plants are highly toxic and as few as one or two seed may have unpleasant effects.

Distributions

The distributions given reflect only those areas where the plants have been collected, but they could well occur elsewhere.

In fact, as will be seen from the distributions, many occur far from the Karoo or even beyond the boundaries of the Republic, and where this is known, it is reflected in the distributions given.

It can, however, be assumed that as the vast majority of the plants were collected near the centre of the Great Karoo, they will occur in varying densities as one approaches the boundaries.

In the text, distribution regions in the Karoo have been divided into 5 summer rainfall areas and 3 winter rainfall areas. The summer rainfall areas are Bushmanland, Northern Karoo, Great Escarpment, Upper Karoo and Great Karoo. The winter rainfall regions are Namaqualand, Tanqua Karoo and the Little Karoo. A ninth region, Cape Fold Belt, lies between the Great and Little Karoo, and does not form part of the Karoo biome.

Veld Types
The veld of the Karoo is broadly divided into four vegetation types. They are dwarf scrub veld, grass veld, tree and shrub veld and ephemeral veld. Grass veld is subdivided again into climax, subclimax and pioneer grasses. The dwarf scrub component is divided into palatable bushes like **koggelmandervoetkaroo** (*Limeum aethiopicum*), **daggapit** (*Nenax microphylla*) and other 4 and 5 star plants; less palatable plants like **anchorkaroo** (*Pentzia incana*), **haarbossie** (*Hirpicium alienatum*) and other 3 star plants, and then the unpalatable plants like **bitterbos** (*Chrysocoma ciliata*), **muistepelkaroo** (*Lightfootia nodosa*) and other 2 star plants. The area dealt with by this book is mainly concerned with dwarf scrub veld. On some of the mountains, to be sure, there are areas that have mixed grass and shrub veld, but this is not a common occurrence at the present time.

The late John Acocks divided the whole country into 70 different Veld Types, and to each he gave a number. The Karoo falls into 19 of them. I have divided this area into 8 different regions (plus a ninth that is not Karoo) for purposes of distribution. They are the following, and each includes those veld types mentioned:

Namaqualand
A winter rainfall region with coastal sandy flats, a mountainous escarpment with a central mountain chain surrounded by open rounded hills and flats, and in the south, an enormous plain (the Knersvlakte) with very saline, shallow soils and small white quartz pebbles. Major Veld Types are Succulent Karoo (Veld Type 31) and Namaqualand Broken Veld (Veld Type 33). Also included are the Strandveld of the West Coast (Veld Type 34) and Mountain Renosterbosveld (Veld Type 43).

Bushmanland
A summer rainfall, high lying inland area consisting of plains, in the north, occasional hills and pans. Soils are shallow red sand underlain by calcrete and dorbank on plains; deep red sands in dunes in the central parts; shallow and stony on hills as well as shallow calcareous and gypsum-rich soils in pans. Major Veld Types are the Arid Karoo (Veld Type 29) and False Succulent Karoo (Veld Type 39).

Northern Karoo
A summer rainfall, high lying inland area consisting of plains, with shallow to moderately deep red sandy soils and hills, with shallow rocky soils. Major Veld Types are Orange River Broken Veld (Veld Type 32) and False Arid Karoo (Veld Type 35). Arid Karoo (Veld Type 29) is also found.

Great Escarpment
A summer rainfall area dividing the low lying and high lying inland areas consisting of low mountains with shallow stony soils, and occasional lowlands with deeper soils. Major Veld Types are Western Mountain Karoo (Veld Type 28), Mountain Renosterbosveld (Veld Type 43) and Karroid *Merxmuellera* Mountain Veld (Veld Type 60). Central Lower Karoo (Veld Type 30), False Karroid Broken Veld (Veld Type 37) and False Orange River Broken Veld (Veld Type 40) are also found.

Upper Karoo
A summer rainfall, high lying inland area consisting of undulating plains, lowlands and hills. The soils are shallow and rocky or red soils on dolerite. Major Veld Types are Central Upper Karoo (Veld Type 27), Arid Karoo (Veld Type 29) and False Upper Karoo (Veld Type 36). False Arid Karoo (Veld Type 35) is also found.

Great Karoo
A summer rainfall, low lying inland area consisting of irregular plains, hills, lowlands and low mountains. Soils are shallow and rocky or deep alluvial sand. Major Veld Types are Karroid Broken Veld (Veld Type 26) and Central Lower Karoo (Veld Type 30). False Central Lower Karoo (Veld Type 38) is also found.

Tanqua Karoo
A summer and winter rainfall, low lying inland area consisting of plains, with shallow rocky soils, as well as deep alluvial soils. Only Succulent Karoo (Veld Type 31) is found here.

Little Karoo
A winter rainfall, low lying inland area consisting of hills, lowlands and occasional silcrete-capped hill tops. The soils are shallow and rocky on the hills and shallow and red in lowlands. Succulent Mountain Scrub [Spekboomveld] (Veld Type 25) and Karroid Broken Veld (Veld Type 26) are found here.

Mountains of the Cape Fold Belt
A winter rainfall, high lying area consisting of high mountains with shallow stony soils. This is not Karoo veld, but is surrounded by Karoo. False Macchia (Veld Type 70), is the major Veld Type, but Mountain Renosterbosveld (Veld Type 43) is also found here.

26

A brief description of each veld type, using Acocks' numbers for identification, follows:

Veld Type 25 Succulent Mountain Scrub.
Typically a dense scrub dominated by *Portulacaria afra* (**spekboom**). Usually steep veld that receives an annual rainfall of between 250 and 300 mm of rain.

Veld Type 26 Karroid Broken Veld
Veld dotted with dwarf trees and shrubs, and including varying amounts of grass and succulents.

(a) The Great Karoo
Succulents are usually relatively scarce, but grass species are surprisingly numerous. There is very little soil in this area. Vegetation is sparse as a result and the shrubs, which are mainly found in the hills, are stunted. Streams and rivers usually have thornveld. The annual rainfall is from 150-200 mm.

(b) The Little Karoo
Succulents are dominant and the dwarf trees and shrubs are numerous. Grasses are scarce. This does not differ from the Great Karoo in any respect other than the number of shrubs and succulents that are found there.

(c) Grassy Mountain Scrub
It is scrub-veld dominated on southern slopes by a dense grassy scrub, while on northern aspects a number of shrubs are found in this grass-scrub mixture.

Veld Type 27 Central Upper Karoo
Hills and mountains are more grassy than the plains. It is a fairly grassy Karoo veld, with the grasses being mainly the 'white' type. The flora is richer in the stony parts than elsewhere. The annual rainfall varies from 200 to 250 mm.

Veld Type 28 Western Mountain Karoo
Soil is conspicuous by its absence. It is a tall, almost non-succulent Karoo growing on very stony country consisting of fine grained sandstone. The annual rainfall varies from 150 to 250 mm.

Veld Type 29 Arid Karoo
By nature it is an even grassier region than the Central Upper Karoo, but the chief species are silvery white desert species. Large shrubs are rare and entirely absent in some areas. It occupies the driest part of the area, with the annual rainfall varying from 100 to 200 mm. This part of the Karoo has been reduced almost to desert by the trekboer.

Veld Type 30 Central Lower Karoo
Flora is much like that of the Arid Karoo, but shorter and denser. *Pentzia incana* (**anchorkaroo**) and some succulents play an important part. Grasses are of the Arid Karoo type. Thornveld along the Kariega River show signs of having been densely grassed. It occupies flat, stony country, and annual rainfall varies from 150-250 mm.

Veld Type 31 Succulent Karoo
This is the veld of the low altitude, hot, arid areas with winter or through the year rainfall. It is dominated by succulents, mainly of the Mesembryanthemaceae. Succulents in this Veld Type vary in growth from almost subterranean stemless dwarfs to 2,5 m high shrubs. Annuals and bulbous plants are numerous.

Veld Type 32 Orange River Broken Veld
This type occupies steep, rocky mountains, on which grow succulents like *Aloe dichotoma* (**kokerboom**) and *Euphorbia avasmontana* (**boesmangif**). This veld occurs on a variety of rocks, such as banded ironstone, dolomite, quartzite and granite. The annual rainfall varies from 150 to 350 mm.

Veld Type 33 Namaqualand Broken Veld
Characterised by dome shaped granite hills and rarer quartzite hills, *Rhigozum trichotomum* (**driedoring**) veld on gravelly plains and grassveld which results from grazing out Karoo bushes. Annual winter rainfall varies from 150 to 300 mm.

Veld Type 34 Strandveld
This is the vegetation of the lower parts of the western coastal plains. It is an open to dense scrub in sandy areas and on the rocky outcrops a variety of smaller bushes are found. Annuals and grasses are found in open spaces between the larger shrubs.

Veld Type 35 False Arid Karoo
It appears to be almost identical with the Arid Karoo, but the plant species found here are slightly different.

Veld Type 36 False Upper Karoo
Flora is much the same as that of the Central Upper Karoo, except that it has more grasses. The area from Murraysburg to Middelburg to De Aar to Colesberg and back encompasses the most spectacular of all changes of vegetation in South Africa. This is an area of grass veld that has been erod-ed into Karoo. There are still pockets here and there that are almost entire-ly grass veld, and these indicate what can be achieved through good, scien-tific farming methods. False Karoo types are inclined to be sparser than the

genuine Karoo types. *Pentzia incana* (**anchorkaroo**) is the dominant karoo bush, and *Chrysocoma ciliata* (**bitterbos**) the main pioneer.

Veld Type 37 False Karroid Broken Veld
Only a small section of this type of veld is to be found in our area. It is taller, denser and slightly less desert-like than the Karroid Broken Veld.

Veld Type 38 False Central Lower Karoo
This small area differs from the previous type because it lacks trees and shrubs, and also lacks the denseness of the Central Lower Karoo, but has the same species.

Veld Type 39 False Succulent Karoo
Inclined to be desert, sparsely populated with members of the Mesembryanthemaceae family and relics of the Arid Karoo.

Veld Type 40 False Orange River Broken Veld
In the Orange River valley and in the Strydenburg area, thickets of **swarthaak** (*Acacia melifera* subsp. *detinens* and **driedoring** (Rhigozum trichotomum) are found. In the valleys and on silty flats succulents become more abundant.

Veld Type 43 Mountain Rhenosterbosveld
The tops of the Nieuweveld and Roggeveld mountain ranges form this type. It does not include all the rhenosterbosveld, but only those parts where *Elytropappus rhinocerotis* (**rhinoceros bush**) does not appear to be an invader. It was much more grassy formerly. It may be that the Mountain Rhenosterbosveld, in its original grassy condition, is to the Fynbos what the thornveld is to the tropical forest, and is to the Karoo what the thornveld is to the Valley Bushveld.

Veld Type 60 Karroid Merxmuellera Mountain Veld
It is closely related to the Mountain Rhenosterbosveld. A sparse, semi-succulent vegetation is found where areas of especially dolerite are found.

Veld Type 70 False Machia
This is not a karroid vegetation.

Habitat
Plant habitats are really pointers to aid the searcher when he is looking for a particular plant. I have divided the area into:
a) Permanent streams – places where there is permanent water available
b) Seasonal streams – most streams in the Karoo fall into this category
c) Flood plains – these are the areas, usually with deep soil, where flood waters open out

d) Flats – these are characterized by a certain amount of soil and a relative absence of stones
e) Apron veld – that piece of the veld just in front of the mountains. It is usually high in minerals, has fairly deep soil and a good number of rocks
f) Rante – as opposed to mountains. Soil will be shallow and there will be an abundance of rocks
g) Mountain slopes – the slopes of mountains as opposed to those of hills
h) Kloofs and wet kloofs – usually found on mountain slopes and through the apron veld
i) Crowns – the tops of the mountains
j) Disturbed areas – those areas that have been disturbed by either man or some other means. Such areas include irrigated lands, roadsides, etc

PLANT DESCRIPTIONS

Grazing values (star ratings)

Grazing values have been given to all plants illustrated in this guide. These have been indicated by stars for quick reference. The scale is as follows:

*****   The very best grazing plant. It must also give an adequate amount of feed.

****   A very good grazing plant that is bettered by only a few.

***   A reasonable plant, but one that is either not of the best quality, or that does not give enough feed.

**   A poor plant that does no harm.

*   A poisonous plant or one that holds other economic disadvantages for the farmer. Noxious weeds are included here.

OPHIOGLOSSACEAE

1 Ophioglossum polyphyllum   **

Small fern resembling a flowering plant. Not grazed.

Namaqualand; Bushmanland; Northern, Great and Upper Karoo and eastern Cape in flood plains.

ADIANTACEAE

2 Adiantum capillus-veneris   maidenhair fern, vrouehaar   **

Fronds remain dry even during a shower as they repel water. Makes a pleasing house plant. Dried fronds smoked to relieve chest colds. Tested negative for antibiotics. An exotic species gave this plant its common name. Not grazed.

Throughout southern Africa in wet, sheltered and shady places such as below waterfalls.

3 Cheilanthes hirta   parsley fern, pietersielievaring   **

Fern seldom reaching more than 15 cm. Decoction used as cure for colds and sore throats. Not grazed.

Widespread throughout southern Africa, mainly in high mountains where mists tend to keep ground moist.

4 Pellaea calomelanos   hard fern, hardevaring   **

Resembles *Pellaea rufa*, except that leaf segments are up to 15 mm in diameter. Smoked by indigenous peoples for relief from asthma and colds. Not grazed.

Great Escarpment; Upper and Great Karoo; southwestern, southern and eastern Cape; western Transvaal and Botswana on mountain slopes.

5 Pellaea rufa   **

Fern with round, bluish-grey leaf segments up to 2 mm in diameter. Black stems. Not grazed.

Great Escarpment; Great and Little Karoo on rante and mountain slopes.

ASPLENIACEAE

6 Asplenium trichomanes   **

Fern with small leaves usually growing at high altitudes. Leaves smoked by indigenous people like tobacco to relieves sore throats and colds. Not grazed.

Great Escarpment on mountain slopes.

7 Ceterach cordatum resurrection fern, opstandingsvaring   **

Fronds curl up and appear dead when dry, but open again if wetted. Somewhat resembles *Cheilanthes eckloniana*, the usual resurrection fern. Not grazed.

Great Escarpment; Upper and Great Karoo; eastern and northern Cape; Orange Free State; Natal; Transvaal; Lesotho and Namibia usually on or near crowns.

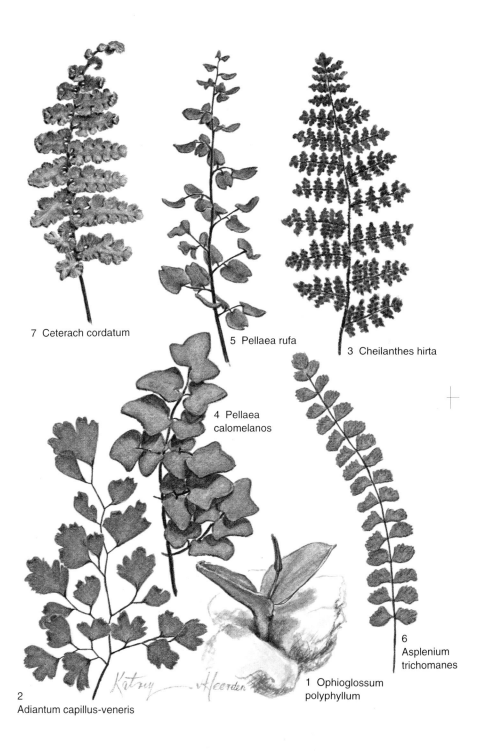

7 Ceterach cordatum

5 Pellaea rufa

3 Cheilanthes hirta

4 Pellaea calomelanos

2 Adiantum capillus-veneris

6 Asplenium trichomanes

1 Ophioglossum polyphyllum

TYPHACEAE
1 **Typha capensis**   bulrush, papkuil   ***
[=Typha latifolia]
Perennial up to 2 m or more. Leaves long, green and strap-shaped. Inflorescence showy, brown and has many female flowers tightly packed together. Male flowers form just above these, but are of shorter duration. Leaves and stems used for rough thatching, and rhizomes were ground to a reddish meal and used to replace cereal meal. High in starch. Very useful for combatting soil erosion by holding back silt in rivers. Grazed to some extent particularly by large stock.

Throughout southern Africa in permanent streams and flood plains.

POACEAE
2 **Phragmites australis**   common reed, fluitjiesriet   ****
[=Phragmites communis]
Water-loving, perennial reed up to 4 m or more. Topped by silky, silver panicle. Root system of creeping rhizomes quick-growing. Very valuable aid in combatting soil erosion by holding back silt in rivers and preventing further disintegration of banks under suitable conditions. Weaver birds fond of nesting in these reeds. Used for rough thatching, while pipes and musical instruments are made from hollow reeds. Young shoots fairly well grazed by large stock, but small stock can graze it only till it reaches a height of about 30 cm.

Throughout southern and tropical Africa in permanent and seasonal streams and flood plains.

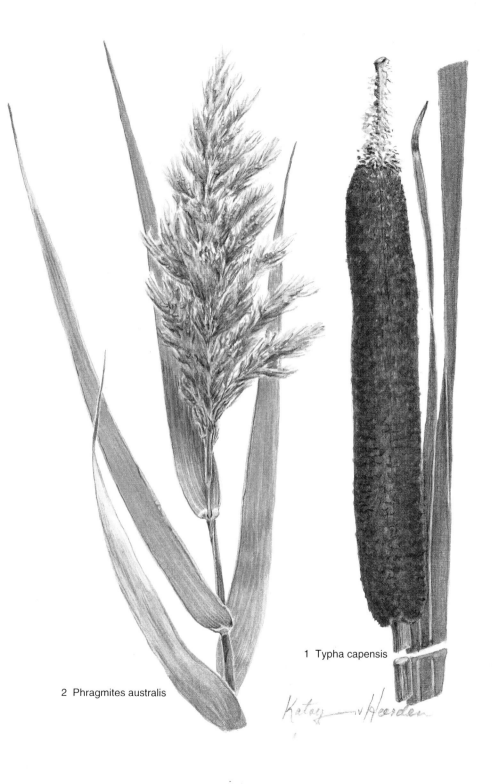

1 Typha capensis

2 Phragmites australis

Katog ——v/Heerden

CYPERACEAE
1 **Cyperus laevigatus**   **
Small sedge seldom exceeding 30 cm. Not grazed.
  Namaqualand; Great Escarpment; Northern, Great, Tanqua and Little Karoo;
southwestern, southern, eastern and northern Cape and Namibia in permanent
streams, wet or damp kloofs. Fairly common in semipermanent moist places.

2 **Cyperus marginatus** matjiesgoed   **
Small sedge up to 75 cm. Rhizomes spread very quickly and can choke small
streams. Useful in combatting soil erosion. Khoisan used this reed for making mats.
Also makes an excellent thatch, and is used for baskets and ropes. Not grazed.
  Throughout southern Africa in permanent and seasonal streams, wet or damp
kloofs and where there are semipermanent moist areas.

3 **Scirpus dioecus** biesie   **
Small rush up to 90 cm. The round, brown balls at the tips of the stem are com-
posed of many flower heads. They grow in damp places, or where the underground water is not too deep, and will die in a drought when water level falls. Not
grazed.
  Throughout arid areas of southern Africa in permanent and seasonal streams,
flood plains and flats.

4 **Pseudoschoenus inanus** hardematjiesgoed   **
[=Scirpus inanus]
Rush up to 2 m. Previously important in riverside plant communities, where it
helped combat soil erosion. Although not scarce, it is no longer as plentiful as it
used to be. Used to thatch houses in pioneer days. Hardly grazed.
  Namaqualand; Great Escarpment; Great Karoo; southwestern, eastern and northern Cape; Orange Free State and Namibia in permanent and seasonal streams, wet
and damp kloofs.

JUNCACEAE
5 **Juncus exsertus** biesie   **
Common rush up to 75 cm. Inflorescence occurs during summer and has branched,
brown heads. Not grazed, but a useful anti-soil erosion plant.
  Great Escarpment; Upper, Great, Tanqua and Little Karoo; southwestern, eastern
and northern Cape; Natal and Transvaal in permanent streams.

6 **Juncus dregeanus** biesie   **
Rush 10-40 cm high. Leaves grass-like. Like other rushes it helps stabilize river
banks. Not grazed.
  Great Escarpment; Upper, Great and Little Karoo; Cape Fold Belt; southwestern,
southern and eastern Cape; Orange Free State; Natal; Transvaal and Lesotho in
water.

7 **Juncus punctorius** biesie   **
Common rush reaching 75 cm. Not grazed, but helps stabilize river banks.
  Great Escarpment; Great and Little Karoo; southwestern, southern, eastern and
northern Cape; Orange Free State; Natal; Transvaal and Namibia in permanent
streams.

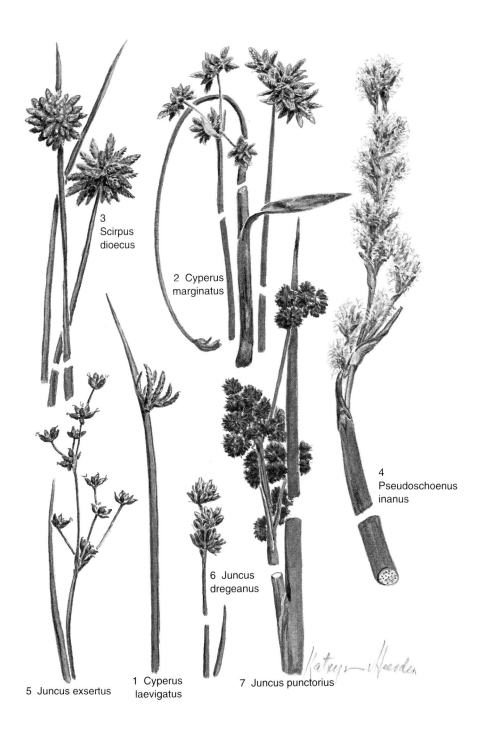

3
Scirpus
dioecus

2 Cyperus
marginatus

4
Pseudoschoenus
inanus

6 Juncus
dregeanus

5 Juncus exsertus

1 Cyperus
laevigatus

7 Juncus punctorius

ASPARAGACEAE
Asparagus species have huge root systems which can aid the combatting of soil erosion. Tubers are used as decoctions for backache, black water and TB among other ailments. Still used by locals for relief of toothache.

1 **Asparagus aethiopicus** haakdoring   **
Lax shrub usually found inside another large shrub for protection. Stems reaching 2,5 m are armed with vicious recurved thorns. Sweet-smelling cream flowers cover entire plant. Young shoots are edible and have been used as vegetables. Not browsed.
   Namaqualand; Great Escarpment; Great, Tanqua and Little Karoo; Cape Fold Belt; southwestern, southern and eastern Cape in a wide range of habitats.

2 **Asparagus capensis** wild asparagus, wag-'n-bietjie   **
Erect to lax shrub up to 1 m, though usually much smaller. Primary stems zig-zag with leaves growing compactly together on short branches. Flowers cream, sweet-smelling and cover whole plant. One of Van Riebeeck's first vegetables at the Cape. Not grazed.
   Namaqualand; Great Escarpment; Upper, Great, Tanqua and Little Karoo; Cape Fold Belt; southwestern and eastern Cape and Namibia in a wide range of habitats.

3 **Asparagus retrofractus**   **
Sprawling shrub reaching almost 3 m, usually found growing inside a tree or other large shrub. Massive root system. Infusion of roots taken several times a day was used by Khoisan for treating pulmonary tuberculosis. Not grazed, but like other trailing varieties, can cause damage to wool and mohair by becoming entangled in fleeces.
   Great Escarpment; Great, Tanqua and Little Karoo; Cape Fold Belt; southwestern, southern and northern Cape and Namibia in a wide range of habitats.

4 **Asparagus striatus** bergappel   **
Erect shrub seldom exceeding 40 cm, though it may grow to 1 m. Has overall dark green colour. Leaves are minute scales and the flattened stems, which are often mistaken for true leaves, end in spines. A riot of white, sweet-smelling flowers appear in late spring. Green fruit turn yellow and finally red when ripe in early summer. Large round green insect galls, later drying to white, often grow on this bush. These are caused by the fly, *Asparagobius braunsi*, which is illustrated. Galls are edible when green and are reputed to be sweet. Exceptionally drought-resistant, but not grazed except under pressure.
   Great Escarpment; Northern, Upper, Great and Little Karoo; eastern and northern Cape; Orange Free State and Namibia in apron veld, rante and mountain slopes.

COLCHICACEAE
5 **Ornithoglossum undulatum** poison onion, Karoo slangkop   *
[Often incorrectly identified as Ornithoglossum viride]
Bulbous plant up to 20 cm. Leaves blue-green and boat-shaped. Flowers point down and petals reflexed. Very poisonous to all livestock and can cause severe losses. Seldom grazed intentionally.
   Throughout southern Africa except Natal; Lesotho and Swaziland in flats, apron veld, rante and mountain slopes.

5 Ornithoglossum undulatum

2 Asparagus capensis

3 Asparagus retrofractus

4 Asparagus striatus

1 Asparagus aethiopicus

ASPARAGACEAE
1 **Asparagus burchellii**   wild asparagus, katbossie, katdoring   **
[=Asparagus sauveolens]
Rambling shrub reaching 2 m. Recurved spines. Edible, and with *Asparagus capensis* formed Van Riebeeck's first vegetables at the Cape. Its root system often stops erosion. Not grazed. Great Escarpment; Great and Little Karoo; Cape Fold Belt; southwestern and southern Cape in a wide range of habitats.

2 **Asparagus mucronatus**   katdoring   **
Erect shrub somewhat resembling a Christmas tree and reaching 2 m. Flowers small, white and sweet-smelling. Roots used by Khoi in treatment of advanced tubercular complaints. Not grazed, but the huge root system helps fight erosion. Namaqualand; Great Escarpment; Great and Little Karoo; southwestern, southern and eastern Cape; Natal; Transvaal and Namibia on rante, mountain slopes and kloofs.

HYACINTHACEAE
3 **Ornithogalum tenuifolium** subsp. **aridum**   **
Bulbous plant of chinkerinchee family appears in great numbers after good rains. Inflorescence has many white flowers. Not grazed, reputedly poisonous. Great Escarpment; Upper and Great Karoo; eastern and northern Cape and Orange Free State in flats.

ALLIACEAE
4 **Tulbaghia leucantha**   wild garlic, fonteinknoffel   **
Clump-forming bulbous plant reaching 20 cm. Strong garlic smell emitted when bruised. All parts used as vegetable or medicinally. Another species, *Tulbaghia alliacea*, which also occurs in the South Western Cape, is slightly larger and does not have the red centre to the flower. Neither are grazed.
   Great Escarpment; Great Karoo; eastern Cape; Orange Free State; Natal and Transvaal in wet or damp kloofs.

ASPHODELACEAE
5 **Bulbine abyssinica**   kopieva   **
Tuberous plant reaching 45 cm. Inflorescence has many yellow flowers on end of a longish flower stalk. Leaves rising roset-like from ground level. Not grazed.
   Namaqualand; Bushmanland; Great Escarpment; Upper, Great, Tanqua and Little Karoo; southwestern and southern Cape; Natal and Orange Free State in apron veld, rante and mountain slopes.

6 **Bulbine frutescens**   snake flower, rankkopieva   **
Tuberous plant up to 30 cm with long, bright green, fleshy leaves, often spiralled. Inflorescence with yellow flowers. Not grazed.
   Namaqualand; Great Escarpment; Upper and Great Karoo; northern, southwestern and eastern Cape; Cape Fold Belt; Orange Free State and Natal on crowns.

7 **Trachyandra thyrsoidea**   veld cabbage, watertoue   **
Long, narrow, fleshy leaves often spiralled. Inflorescence with white and brown flowers. Among first South African plants to be illustrated in colour in Holland. Used medicinally and as a vegetable. Usually grows in sandy soil. Hardly grazed.
   Namaqualand; Great Escarpment; Little Karoo; southwestern, southern and eastern Cape on mountain slopes and kloofs.

40

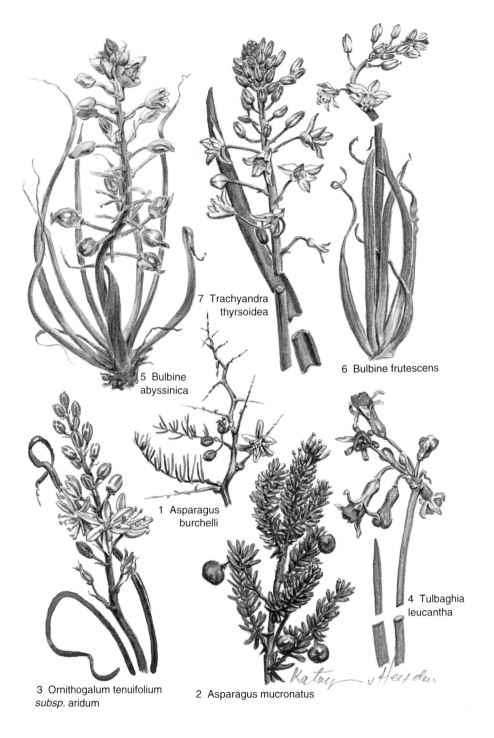

7 Trachyandra
thyrsoidea

6 Bulbine frutescens

5 Bulbine
abyssinica

1 Asparagus
burchelli

4 Tulbaghia
leucantha

3 Ornithogalum tenuifolium
subsp. aridum

2 Asparagus mucronatus

ASPHODELACEAE

1 **Aloe longistyla** Karoo aloe, ramenas   **

Small stemless aloe up to 25 cm. Leaves, which are sometimes spotted, have spines on their edges. Unbranched inflorescence appears in midwinter, and bears coral to rose-red flowers. Not grazed.

   Great Escarpment; Upper, Great and Little Karoo and eastern Cape in flats, apron veld and rante.

2 **Aloe striata** coral aloe, gladdeblaaraalwyn   **

Usually stemless aloe up to 60 cm. Some older plants have prostrate stems. Leaves vary from greenish-grey to dusty-pink with distinct coral stripes down the edges. One of very few Southern African species that does not have spines on edge of leaf. Branched inflorescence appears during winter and early spring. Individual flowers a deep coral. Not grazed.

   Great Escarpment; Great and Little Karoo; Cape Fold Belt; southern and eastern Cape in flats, apron veld, rante and mountain slopes.

3 **Aloe variegata** variegated aloe, kanniedood   **

Small, usually stemless aloe reaching 25 cm. Seldom found growing singly as it suckers from roots. Clearly spotted leaves are arranged in three rows six to ten deep, often with small spines along the edges. Inflorescence, which appears in spring, is single, and flowers vary from light to dark coral-pink. Used medicinally for curing sores on fingers. According to an old superstition, if someone transplants one of these aloes and it dies, that person will die too. Not grazed, though porcupines dig them out in great numbers.

   Throughout Karoo; southern Orange Free State and Namibia in flats and apron veld.

4 **Kniphofia uvaria** red-hot poker, vuurpyl   **

Plant up to 75 cm. Flowers during summer. Oldest-known red-hot poker. Genus named after Kniphof, a botanist who first drew the flower. Gardeners cultivated it generally from about 1800. Decoction made from crushed bulb used as an enema. Not grazed.

   Namaqualand; Great Escarpment; Cape Fold Belt; southwestern and eastern Cape in kloofs and crowns.

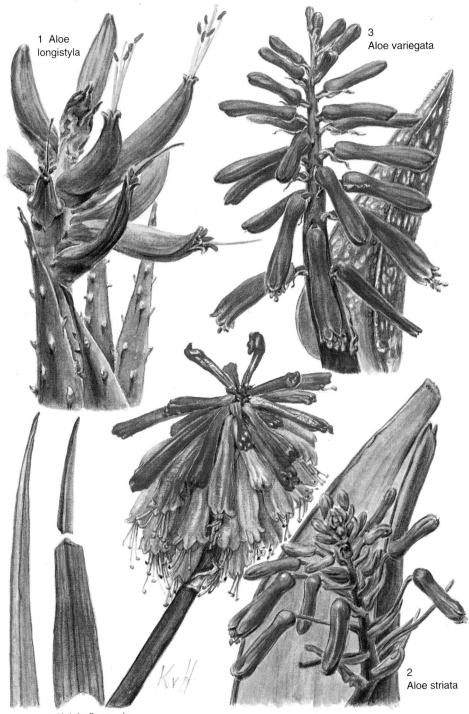

1 Aloe
longistyla

3
Aloe variegata

2
Aloe striata

4 Kniphofia uvaria

KvH

ASPHODELACEAE

1 Aloe aristata   baard-aalwyn   **

Small aloe up to 40 cm in diameter and height. Leaves form a rosette, and it can be mistaken for a species of *Haworthia*. Not grazed.

Great Escarpment; eastern Cape; Orange Free State; Natal and Lesotho on mountain slopes and crowns.

2 Aloe broomii   mountain aloe, bergaalwyn   **

Large aloe up to 2 m. Not all flowers on spike open simultaneously. Buds and open flowers completely hidden by bracts. Spring-flowering. Boiled juice used as a cattle dip during last century. One of only two aloes recorded in Bushman paintings. Not grazed.

Great Escarpment; Upper Karoo; eastern and northern Cape and Orange Free State in apron veld, hill and mountain slopes and crowns.

3 Aloe claviflora   kanonaalwyn, kraalaalwyn   **

Usually stemless aloe reaching 45 cm. Leaves densely packed and fairly long (20-30 cm). Spines occur on edges with a few isolated ones on top third of back of leaf. Usually branchless inflorescence lies at an angle, often almost horizontal to ground. Individual flowers orange-red. As plant ages it sends out new plants from base that grow in a circle. Eventually they form a ring or 'kraal' once plants in centre have died. Not grazed.

Namaqualand; Bushmanland; Great Escarpment; Upper and Great Karoo; northern Cape and Namibia in flats, apron veld and rante.

4 Aloe microstigma   **

Aloe up to 30 cm. Green to reddish leaves with white spots form a rosette. Usually short-stemmed. Individual flowers usually yellow, but may be red or even red and yellow. Not grazed.

Great Escarpment; Tanqua and Little Karoo; southern and eastern Cape and Namibia in rante and mountain slopes.

5 Aloe striatula   **

Aloe up to 1,8 m. May be recognized by its bright green, glossy leaves, stripes on leaf sheaths and dense inflorescences. Flowers slightly curved. Not grazed.

Great Escarpment and eastern Cape on mountain slopes and crowns.

6 Gasteria disticha   bontaalwyn, beestong   **

Aloe-like bulbous plant with rounded leaves and long flower-stalk. Inflorescence pink, and individual flowers much resemble those of aloes. Not grazed.

Great Escarpment; Great Karoo; southwestern and southern Cape in rante.

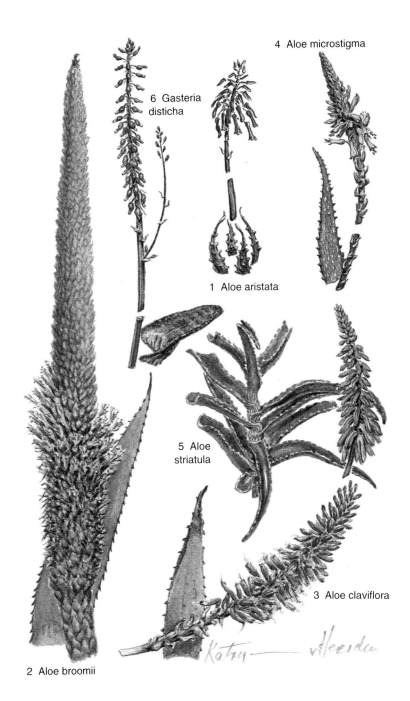

4 Aloe microstigma

6 Gasteria disticha

1 Aloe aristata

5 Aloe striatula

3 Aloe claviflora

2 Aloe broomii

ASPHODELACEAE
1 **Trachyandra acocksii**   wildeseldery   **
Bulbous plant up to 45 cm. Inflorescence can be used as a vegetable. Not much grazed.
Restricted to escarpment north of Beaufort West in rante.

HYACINTHACEAE
2 **Albuca setosa**   snotblom   **
Bulbous plant up to 50 cm. Inflorescence on end of a fairly long stalk. Leaves and flower stalk exude mucilaginous fluid when broken or cut. Not grazed.
Great Escarpment and Great Karoo in flats, apron veld, rante and mountain slopes.

3 **Albuca** sp.   **
Small bulbous plant having narrow leaves bunched at base. Brown and white flower on a stalk about 10 cm long. Not grazed.
Great Escarpment and Great Karoo in rante.

4 **Veltheimia capensis**   quarobe, sandlelie   **
Bulbous plant, winter-flowering, growing in clumps up to 45 cm. Inflorescence somewhat resembles a red-hot poker's, but is pinker. Name 'quarobe' is of Namaqua origin. First mentioned in Van der Stel's journal in 1685 which noted that the bulb had a purgative effect, making it one of the oldest Southern African plants to have its medicinal value recorded. Whole plant well grazed by small stock.
Namaqualand; Great Escarpment; Great, Tanqua and Little Karoo; southwestern and southern Cape in rante.

AMARYLLIDACEAE
5 **Strumaria gemmata**   **
[=*Hessea gemmata*]
Small bulbous plant found in rocky situations and limestone flats. Not very common, and not grazed.
Great, Upper Karoo and Little Karoo; southwestern, southern and eastern Cape in flats and rante.

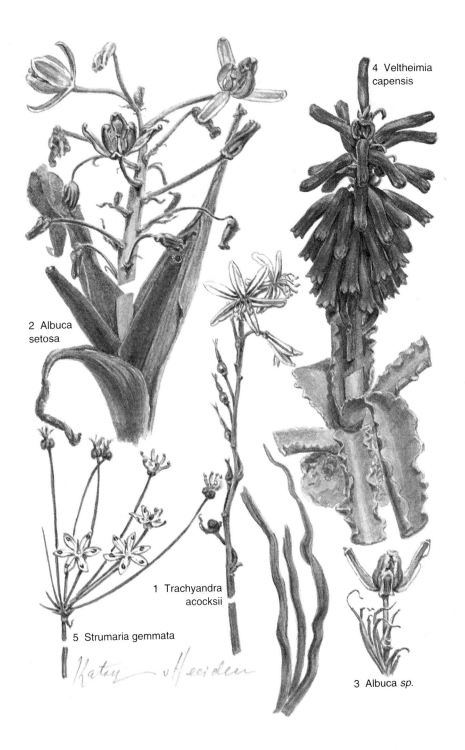

4 Veltheimia
capensis

2 Albuca
setosa

1 Trachyandra
acocksii

5 Strumaria gemmata

3 Albuca *sp.*

COLCHICACEAE
1 **Androcymbium melanthioides**   patrysblom   **
Grows from corms. Found in large numbers where it occurs. Usually not more than 12 cm. Flower-heads made up of bracts enclosing several pale cream flowers. Partridges eat corms, but otherwise not grazed.
   Great Escarpment; Nothern, Upper and Great Karoo; southern, eastern and northern Cape; Transvaal; Orange Free State and Namibia on crowns.

AMARYLLIDACEAE
2 **Ammocharis coranica**   berglelie, gifbol   *
Leaves spread out flat and are about 40 cm long and 5 cm wide. Inflorescence appears on stalk about 40 cm long. Grows in sandy areas. Whole plant and bulb very poisonous to all livestock. Not grazed.
   Upper Karoo; Great and Little Karoo; southern, eastern and northern Cape; Orange Free State; Transvaal and Namibia in flats.

IRIDACEAE
3 **Tritonia karooica**   aandblom   **
Small bulbous plant up to 8 cm. Appears in great numbers in spring. Leaves fan-shaped. Flowers shades of yellow, orange and brown. Sweet-smelling, and gives off a very strong perfume, especially at night. Not grazed.
   Bushmanland; Great Escarpment; Northern, Upper and Great Karoo in rante.

4 **Homeria miniata**   poison bulb, kraaitulp, geeltulp   **
Bulbous plant up to 50 cm. Regarded by some as poisonous, but usually only taken by animals that come from an area where it does not occur. A poisonous species, *Homeria pallida*, also grows in the area. Distinguished by its single leaf, whereas *H. miniata* has two. Hardly grazed.
   Namaqualand; Bushmanland; Great Escarpment; Upper, Great, Tanqua and Little Karoo; southwestern and southern Cape and Namibia in apron veld, rante and mountain slopes.

5 **Moraea polystachya**   bloutulp   *
Bulbous plant up to 75 cm. Bears striking purple flowers. Not usually grazed, though cattle sometimes take it with grass growing nearby. Very poisonous though reports have been received that corms are edible and leaves grazed in the Tanqua Karoo.
   Great Escarpment; Northern, Upper, Great, Tanqua and Little Karoo; Cape Fold Belt; southwestern, southern, eastern and northern Cape; Orange Free State; Transvaal; Botswana, Namibia and Zimbabwe in flats.

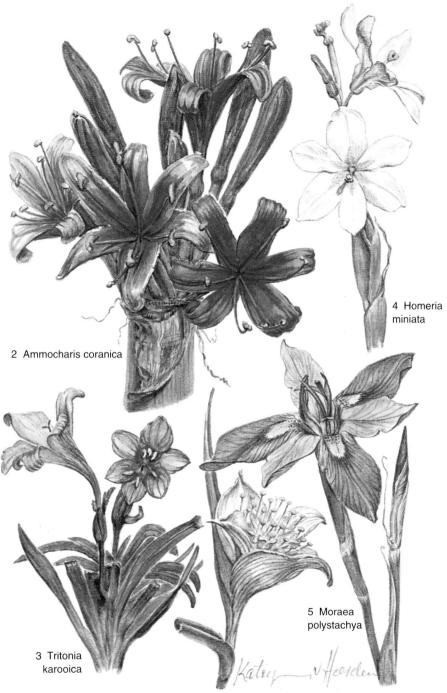

4 Homeria
miniata

2 Ammocharis coranica

3 Tritonia
karooica

5 Moraea
polystachya

1 Androcymbium melanthioides

IRIDACEAE
1 **Babiana hypogea**   bobbejaanuintjie   **
Has several stiff, ribbed leaves, sometimes spiralled. Deep blue flowers. Corm is edible and leaves are grazed.
   Great Escarpment; Great and Tanqua Karoo and northern Cape in rante usually in rock cracks.

SALICACEAE
2 **Salix babylonica**   weeping willow, treurwilg   ****
Naturalized exotic introduced from Europe though originating from Asia. Tree up to 25 m. Has long, trailing shoots that hang downwards. Branches root very easily, so it may be propagated freely. Highly prized ornamental tree and also excellent fodder eagerly sought by all livestock. Well-known for its medicinal properties, and is often used to treat sick geese.
   Cosmopolitan on river banks and dams.

3 **Salix mucronata** subsp. **capensis**   Cape willow, rivierwilg   ***
Fast-growing tree reaching 12 m. Easily propagated from cuttings. Windblown seed does not remain viable for any length of time. A valuable fodder tree grazed by all types of livestock.
   Throughout the Cape, Orange Free State; Transvaal; Lesotho and Namibia in permanent streams, wet or damp kloofs.

URTICACEAE
4 **Forsskaolea candida**   kwaaibul   ***
Erect herb to 50 cm. Stems red and covered with fine, soft thorns. Leaves dark green above and white-woolly below with irregular margins. Grows mainly on roadsides and under cliffs where animals cannot reach it easily. Used medicinally, especially for headaches, 'flu' and stomach complaints. Well grazed, though not palatable in the Tanqua Karoo and Namaqualand.
   Namaqualand; Bushmanland; Great Escarpment; Northern, Upper, Great and Tanqua Karoo; northern Cape and Namibia in seasonal streams, mountain slopes and disturbed areas.

5 **Urtica urens**   small stinging nettle, klein brandnetel   **
Exotic from Europe probably introduced at a very early date. Erect annual up to 60 cm. Large leaves have coarsely serrated margins. Stinging hairs cover whole plant. Many people use it as a pot-herb or as a spinach. Has also been very widely used medicinally. Grazed by sheep and goats.
   Widespread in southern Africa in disturbed areas.

2 Salix babylonica

1 Babiana
hypogea

5 Urtica urens

4 Forsskaolea candida

3 Salix mucronata *subsp*. capensis

LORANTHACEAE

All members of this family are parasites. Hosts are usually from *Acacia*, *Rhus*, *Lycium* and *Salix* genera, although sometimes they are found on other shrubs and trees.

1 **Moquinella rubra**   lighted candles mistletoe, vuurhoutjievoëlent   ***
[=Loranthus elegans]
Common mistletoe growing on a great variety of hosts. Stems very brittle. Leaves up to 6 cm long. Flowers resemble orange matches with tip turning from green to black when ripe. A jerk or tap causes petals to turn back and eject pollen. Winter-flowering, and provides a beautiful splash of colour in otherwise barren veld. Well grazed by all livestock, but can be poisonous if it was parasitic on poisonous *Melianthus comosus* (kruidjie-roer-my-niet).
    Namaqualand; Great Escarpment; Northern, Upper, Great and Little Karoo; Cape Fold Belt; southwestern, southern and eastern Cape and Namibia in a wide range of habitats.

2 **Septulina glauca**   mistletoe, voëlent   **
Usually occurring on species of *Lycium* or *Rhus*. Leaves have greyish appearance. Flowers greyish-green tipped with dull red. Hardly grazed.
    Namaqualand; Great Escarpment; Upper, Great and Little Karoo; southwestern, southern and northern Cape; Orange Free State and Namibia in seasonal streams, flats, rante and kloofs.

VISCACEAE

3 **Viscum continuum**   mistletoe, voëlent   ***
Leafless, green mistletoe only on species of *Acacia*. Has rudimentary scales and forms a dense rounded cluster up to 1 m in diameter. Young shoots often only half as wide as primaries. Round fruits whitish to transparent. Widely used medicinal-ly. *Viscum capense* is similar, but has a slightly wider distribution. Does not usually exceed 50 cm in diameter and parasitizes many host plants, including *Acacia*, *Lycium*, *Rhus* and *Salix* species. Well grazed, and during droughts trees containing these parasites are chopped as feed for livestock.
    Great Escarpment; Great and Little Karoo; southern, eastern and northern Cape in a wide range of habitats.

4 **Viscum rotundifolium**   mistletoe, tee, voëlent   **
Usually parasitic on *Maytenus*, *Carissa* and *Lycium* species. Stems and leaves vary from dark to light green. Leaves almost oval. Sticky, round fruits varying from yel-low, through orange to red, stick to birds' beaks or pass through them within min-utes, carrying the seed to the nest host. Has been used to make tea, while juice has been rubbed on to warts. Hardly grazed.
    Widespread in southern Africa in permanent and seasonal streams, flats, apron veld, rante, mountain slopes and kloofs.

SANTALACEAE

5 **Thesium triflorum**   gifbossie   *
Sprawling shrub usually found growing inside larger plants. Branches brittle. If consumed by animals accidently, can have fatal effects. Great Escarpment; south-ern and eastern Cape in seasonal streams, apron veld and mountain slopes.

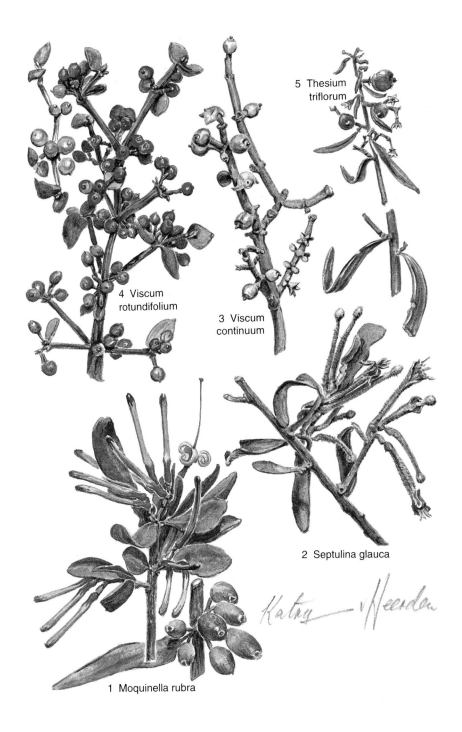

5 Thesium triflorum

4 Viscum rotundifolium

3 Viscum continuum

2 Septulina glauca

1 Moquinella rubra

SANTALACEAE
1 **Thesium lineatum** witstorm, vaalstorm   **** or *
Shrubby root parasite up to 1,5 m. Young, olive-green branches look like broom
bristles. Branches covered with minute leaves and small, insignificant green and
yellow flowers after rains. Fruit white and round. One of the most drought-resistant plants in the Karoo that flowers even in a drought. Many farmers believe it to
be poisonous and systematically destroy it. Paradoxically tests show some plants to
be innocuous and others to contain a toxin similar to that in *Moraea, Melianthus* and
Ornithoglossum. The author suspects that the toxicity of this plant is dependant
upon which plants it has parasitized. Very eagerly grazed by all types of stock.
    Widespread in arid areas of southern Africa on a wide range of habitats.

CHENOPODIACEAE
2 **Atriplex lindleyi** subsp. **inflata**   Australian saltbush, blasiebrak   **
[=*Blackiella inflata*]
Naturalized exotic (sometimes an invader) from Australia, introduced to South
Africa to help fight erosion and to provide feed on saline soils. Dwarf shrub up to
30 cm high. Leaves light blue-green. Masses of released inflated sponge-like capsules containing seed tend to smother other seedlings. Not very palatable in many
areas.
    Widespread in arid areas of southern Africa on flats, disturbed areas and particu-
larly on pans.

3 **Atriplex nummularia**   old man's saltbush, oumansoutbos   ***
Introduced Australian saltbush extensively planted as a drought-resistant fodder
for livestock. Shrub up to 3 m high. Leaves silver-grey. Inflorescence yellow or
pink. High salt content makes it unpalatable, but new varieties containing less salt
are better grazed. Its palatability and usefulness are contentious.
    Cultivated widely in the arid areas of southern Africa.

4 **Atriplex semibaccata**   creeping saltbush, kruipsoutbos   ****
Doubtful whether indigenous. Prostrate. Produces masses of red fruit that germinate easily. Very palatable. Regarded as valuable fodder.
    Widespread in arid areas of southern Africa in seasonal streams and a wide
range of habitats.

5 **Atriplex vestita**   Cape saltbush, klappiesbrak, vaalbrak   ****
Shrub up to 1,2 m. Leaves silvery-grey. Flowers light yellow. Seed winged. Very
well grazed in many areas, but in others unpalatable.
    Namaqualand; Bushmanland; Great Escarpment; Northern, Upper, Great,
Tanqua and Little Karoo; southwestern, southern and eastern Cape and Namibia in
seasonal streams, flood plains and flats.

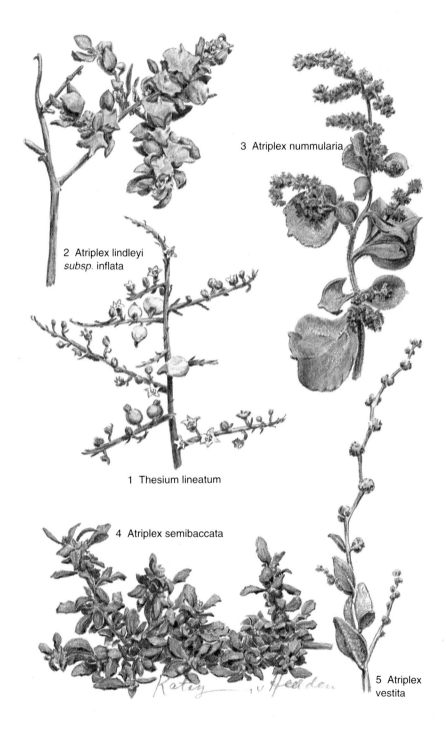

3 Atriplex nummularia

2 Atriplex lindleyi
subsp. inflata

1 Thesium lineatum

4 Atriplex semibaccata

5 Atriplex
vestita

CHENOPODIACEAE

1 Exomis microphylla   brakbossie, hondepisbossie   ***

Shrub up to 90 cm. Flowers mostly hidden by bracts. Often used as an indicator plant as it grows chiefly on brackish soils. Well grazed.

Great Karoo; southwestern and southern Cape in rante.

2 Salsola aphylla   lye bush, rivierganna, loogasganna   *****

Shrub up to 4 m, though usually grazed down to between 1 and 2 m. Stems dark, gnarled and brittle. Leaves small, succulent and bunched tightly on tips of younger shoots. Flowers small, green-yellow and tightly clustered. Often grows on floodplains next to rivers. Ash produces a strong lye for soap making. White insect galls often mistaken for seed. Very well grazed. Animals tend to strip leaves from stems, giving it a bedraggled appearance.

Namaqualand; Bushmanland; Great Escarpment; Northern, Great and Little Karoo; southwestern, southern and northern Cape; Orange Free State; Transvaal; Botswana and Namibia in seasonal streams and flood plains.

3 Salsola calluna   rooilootganna, swartganna   *****

[=Salsola nigrescens]

Shrub to 30 cm. Minute yellow flowers. Hard, fleshy leaves. Young stems have distinctive red colour. A hard and scruffy bush, it is surprising that all types of animals graze it eagerly. Greatly reduced by overstocking, but judicious sparing of veld allows regeneration.

Great Escarpment; Northern, Upper and Great Karoo; eastern and northern Cape and Orange Free State in flats, apron veld and rante.

4 Salsola kali   tumble weed, rolbos   **

Exotic ephemeral originating from Europe and Asia. Round growth form to 1 m. When dry breaks off at ground level and rolls along in wind till stopped. Reasonably palatable when young when its nutritional value is high, but not grazed when older.

Widespread in arid areas of southern Africa in flood plains and disturbed areas.

5 Salsola smithii   inkbos   ***

Shrub to 1,5 m. Like *Suaeda fruticosa*, another ink bush that it closely resembles, it replaces river gannas (*Salsola* species). The main difference is that *Suaeda* leaves occur in threes, while *Salsola* leaves occur singly. Fairly well grazed.

Great Escarpment and Orange Free State in seasonal streams and flood plains.

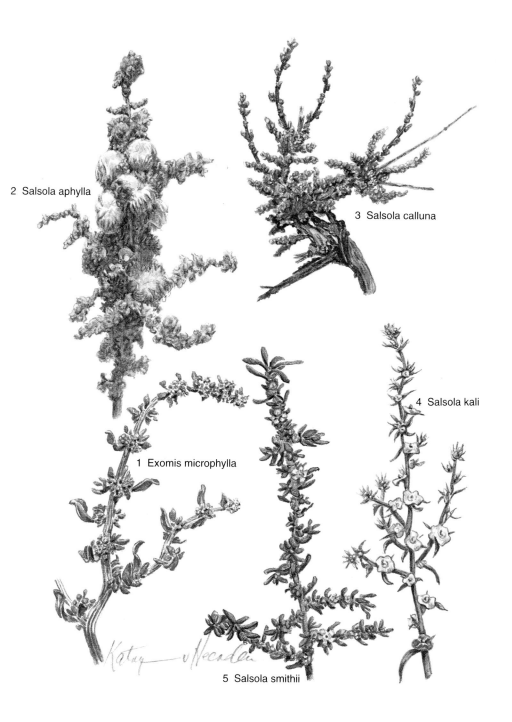

2 Salsola aphylla

3 Salsola calluna

4 Salsola kali

1 Exomis microphylla

5 Salsola smithii

CHENOPODIACEAE
1 **Salsola dealata** ganna ****
Shrub usually not exceeding 30 cm. Very well grazed.
   Great Escarpment in rante.

AMARANTHACEAE
2 **Sericocoma avolans** gras-bo-bos-onder, katstert ****
Dwarf shrub to 40 cm. Inflorescence, which appears on a long stem, resembles a tuft of grass. Has been used in treatment of rheumatism. Well grazed.
   Bushmanland; Great Escarpment; Northern, Upper, Great, Tanqua and Little Karoo; northern Cape and Namibia in rante and mountain slopes.

AIZOACEAE
3 **Tetragonia sarcophylla** kinkelbos ****
Shrub up to 2 m. Leaves slightly succulent. Flowers yellow. Fruit 4-winged. Other *Tetragonia* species much resembles this one but their growth forms vary from small compact shrubs to rambling climbers. Usually very palatable.
   Namaqualand; Great Escarpment; Great and Little Karoo; southwestern, southern and eastern Cape in apron veld, rante and mountain slopes.

4 **Hypertelis salsoloides** volstruisbrak, braksuring ***
Herb to 30 cm. Longish, blue-green leaves round in section with a sour taste. Has been used in salads. Usually grazed flat. Even in this state it produces masses of seed that can germinate in favourable conditions.
   Throughout arid areas of southern Africa in flats and rante.

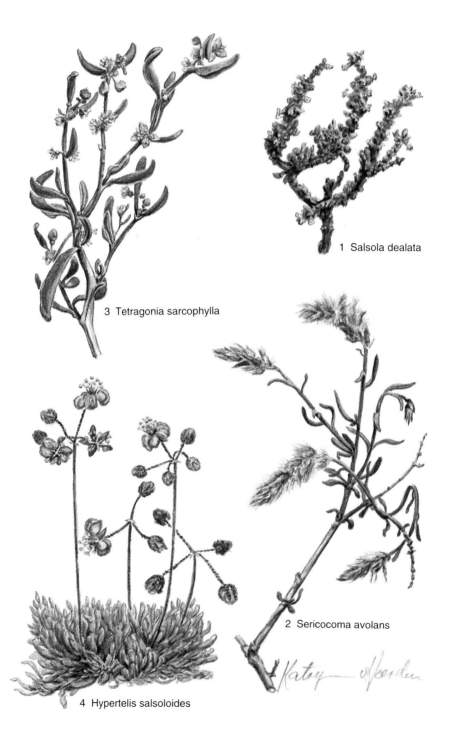

1 Salsola dealata

3 Tetragonia sarcophylla

2 Sericocoma avolans

4 Hypertelis salsoloides

AIZOACEAE
1 **Galenia africana** var. **secundata**   yellow bush, geelbos   ***
A sprawling shrub less than 75 cm with a yellow-green appearance. Flowers
among the leaves. Well grazed.
 Namaqualand; Great Escarpment; Northern Karoo and northern Cape in flats,
apron veld and rante.

Galenia africana var. **africana**   kraalbos   *
(Not illustrated)
Upright shrub to 1 m. Stems smooth and light brown. Leaves longer, narrower and
more yellow than *Galenia africana* var. *secundata*. Individual minute yellowish flowers on the outer edge of bush. Occurs in waste and disturbed ground, and areas
where veld has been overgrazed. Indications are that it is spreading. Pioneers
soaked it in a lye made from *Psilocaulon* species and the resulting mixture was used
to scrub kitchen tables to give them a beautiful yellow appearance. Not usually
grazed, and can cause dropsy in smallstock.
 Widespread throughout the Cape and Namibia in seasonal streams, flats, rante
and disturbed areas.

2 **Galenia fruticosa**   vanwyksbos   **
Shrub to 25 cm. Leaves usually grey to grey-green. Flowers pink or yellow. Fairly
well grazed.
 Namaqualand; Great Escarpment; Upper, Great and Little Karoo; southwestern
and southern Cape and Namibia in flats, apron veld and rante.

3 **Galenia sarcophylla**   vanwyksbrak   ****
Prostrate, perennial herb covering, in good times, up to a square meter. Stems and
branches juicy, and usually a reddish colour. Pink, or sometimes yellow, flowers
solitary, but in great numbers. Thrives on brackish soils. Very readily grazed.
 Namaqualand; Bushmanland; Great Escarpment; Upper, Great, Tanqua and
Little Karoo; southwestern, southern, eastern and northern Cape; Orange Free State
and Namibia in flats and rante.

4 **Limeum aethiopicum**   koggelmandervoetkaroo   *****
Low-growing shrub with a huge root system, seldom more than 20 cm high,
although in spared veld it can reach more than three times that size. The crown is a
mass of closely-packed branches covered with small, dark green leaves arranged in
the shape of small hands like those of the agama lizard (koggelmander). After rains
it sends out shoots and flowers appear on the tips. Seed is then formed and must
stay on the plant for a couple of months before becoming fertile. Exceptionally
drought resistant with very good regrowth. Probably the most palatable plant in
the Karoo.
 Widespread in arid areas in a wide range of habitats.

5 **Plinthus karooicus**   silver Karoo, silwer-Karoo, Karoo-ganna   *****
Shrub to 30 cm high and slightly broader. Fine silver hairs cover slightly succulent
leaves. Very small yellow flowers. Seed does not germinate easily, but survival rate
is good. Very drought resistant and very well grazed.
 Great Escarpment; Upper and Great Karoo; Northern Cape; Orange Free State
and Botswana in rante.

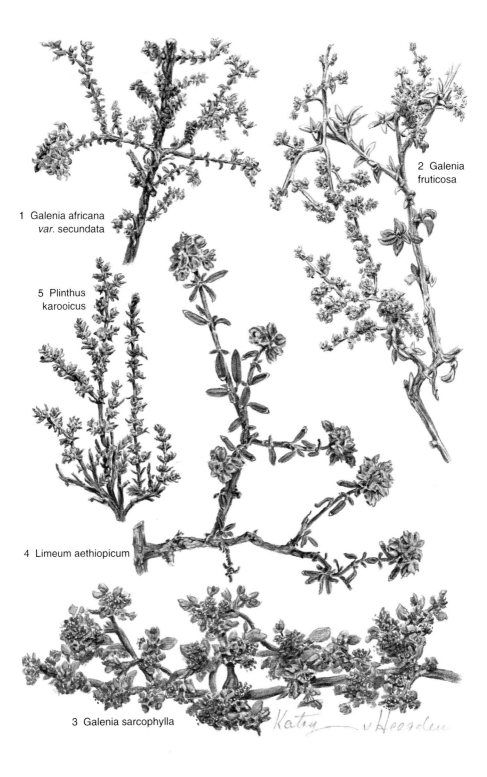

1 Galenia africana
  var. secundata

2 Galenia
  fruticosa

5 Plinthus
  karooicus

4 Limeum aethiopicum

3 Galenia sarcophylla

Katy   v Heerden

MESEMBRYANTHEMACEAE

1 Delosperma sp. doringlose vygie ****
Shrub to 50 cm if sheltered. Stems reddish-brown and shiny. Leaves succulent.
Flowers white. Another, almost identical species with the same common name, has
purple flowers. When disturbed leaves tend to fall off. Very well grazed.
Great Escarpment; Tanqua and Little Karoo in flats, apron veld and rante.

2 Eberlanzia ferox doringvygie, steekvy **
Very common leaf succulent shrub to 30 cm. Branches intertwine and have many
spines, some up to 5 cm long, which makes it difficult to pull apart. Flowers purple.
Fruit woody with segments opening to expel seed during rain. It develops leaves
and flowers with extreme rapidity after rain has fallen. Its value as a fodder plant is
then at its greatest. Well grazed at times.
Throughout arid areas of southern Africa in flats, apron veld and rante.

3 Hereroa stanleyi **
Small succulent up to 5 cm. Flowers yellow. Not grazed.
Great Escarpment in flats and rante.

4 Pleiospilos compactus kwaggavy, volstruistoon ***
Small succulent with characteristic glandular leaves. Large yellow flowers open in
late afternoon. Seed in a woody capsules with segments that open and expel seeds
during rain. They remain on plant for a long time. Often found in far greater numbers than expected owing to its inconspicuous form and ease of germination. Very
palatable.
Great Escarpment; Great and Little Karoo in flats and rante.

5 Sceletium emarcidum kougoed **
Succulent herb to 25 cm. After flowering the 'skeleton' remains for many months.
Some farmers believe that if their animals have *Sceletium* in their diet, they can go
14 days without water. Has medicinal properties, especially as a sedative. If used
just after fermentation it will cause drunkenness. Khoisan chewed roots to anaes-
thetize their lower jaws before extracting teeth. Hardly grazed.
Namaqualand; Great Escarpment; Great and Upper Karoo in flats, apron veld
and rante.

6 Trichodiadema setuliferum hairy nipple vygie, stervygie ****
Leaf succulent shrub to 50 cm. Leaves occur on tips of branches and have hairs
characteristically arranged in a star shaped point. Flowers bright purple. Very well
grazed.
Great Escarpment and Great Karoo in rante and mountain slopes.

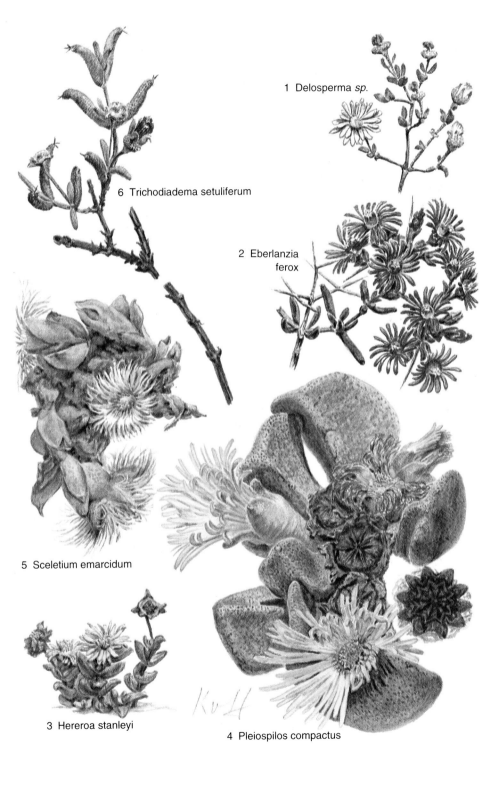

1 Delosperma *sp.*

6 Trichodiadema setuliferum

2 Eberlanzia ferox

5 Sceletium emarcidum

3 Hereroa stanleyi

4 Pleiospilos compactus

MESEMBRYANTHEMACEAE

1 **Drosanthemum archeri**   **

Prostrate leaf succulent reaching 30 cm in diameter. Purple and white flowers very showy. Grazed to some extent.

Great Escarpment; Great and Little Karoo and southern Cape in seasonal streams, flats, apron veld and rante, preferring sandy soils, and requiring some moisture.

2 **Malephora crocea**   copper vygie, vingerkanna   **

Leaf succulent up to 40 cm. Succulent green leaves are heavy. Flowers large and bright yellow-orange. Grazed to some extent.

Namaqualand; Bushmanland; Great Escarpment; Great Karoo; southwestern and northern Cape in seasonal streams, flood plains, flats and disturbed areas.

3 **Mesembryanthemum guerichianum**   ice plant, brakslaai   **

Grows to 20 cm with a spread of 4 times as much. Leaves large and whole plant is covered in glittering, round water cells resembling dewdrops. Light yellow or pink flowers open in bright sunlight. They are of the 'vygie' type and a favorite of bees. A solution made from dried or fresh leaves removes hair from skins in the tanning process. Not much grazed, and can cause oxalic acid poisoning.

Throughout the Karoo; southwestern Cape and Namibia in permanent and seasonal streams, flood plains, flats, apron veld, rante and disturbed areas.

4 **Psilocaulon** sp.   asbos, seepbossie   **

Shrub up to 1 m. Stems jointed and succulent. Leaves minute. Ash used extensively in soap making in frontier days. A similar species, *Psilocaulon absimile*, was also used in the tanning process, and was the principal source of alkaline lye during the first World War. Hardly grazed.

Throughout the Karoo; southern, eastern and northern Cape and Namibia in seasonal streams, flood plains, flats and disturbed areas.

5 **Psilocaulon utile**   asbos, loogbos   **

Prostrate annual. Can cover almost a square meter in favourable conditions. Like other members of this genus, *Psilocaulon utile* is used as a source of alkali and also in the tanning process. Grazed to some extent.

Bushmanland; Great Escarpment; Great and Little Karoo in flats and rante.

6 **Aridaria splendens**   donkievygie   ****

Leaf succulent shrub up to 1,25 m. Often only survives inside other bushes, especially *Lycium* species. Very palatable, and eagerly grazed by large stock, particularly donkeys.

Great Escarpment; Great, Tanqua and Little Karoo in rante, mountain slopes and crowns.

7 **Delosperma** sp.   vygie   ***

One of many small vygies growing throughout the Karoo. Most species of *Delosperma* are grazed, some fairly well.

Great Escarpment in seasonal streams, and flats.

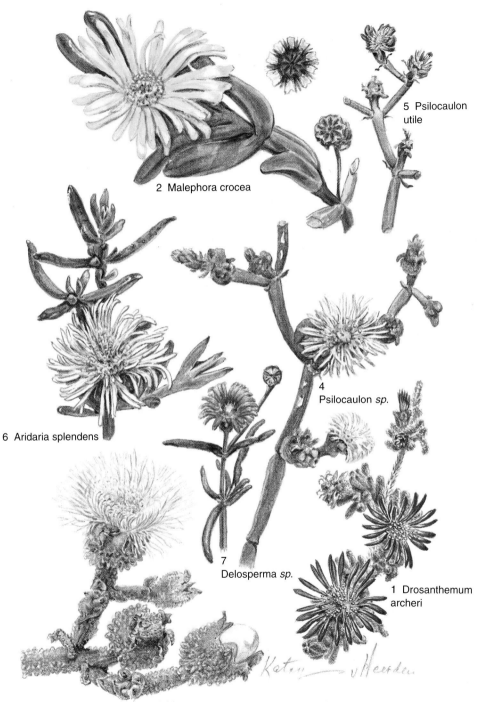

5 Psilocaulon utile

2 Malephora crocea

4 Psilocaulon *sp.*

6 Aridaria splendens

7 Delosperma *sp.*

1 Drosanthemum archeri

3 Mesembryanthemum guerichianum

MESEMBRYANTHEMACEAE
1 **Mesembryanthemum** sp.   vybos   **
Succulent growing in great numbers after good rains. Of very little value to the
stock farmer while still green, but sheep do graze it, especially during winter
months once it has dried off.
Great Escarpment and Great Karoo in flats.

2 **Ruschia paucifolia**   skilpadvygie   **
Succulent shrub up to 25 cm with diameter of up to 1 m. Succulent, greenish leaves.
Bright red flowers may cover plant in early summer. Not grazed.
Great Escarpment; Upper Karoo and Cape Fold Belt on crowns.

PORTULACACEAE
3 **Anacampseros ustulata**   moerbossie, kirriemoer   **
Small succulent resembling goose droppings. Stems whitish and seldom longer
than 5 cm. Tuberous rootstock widely used as yeast supplement in beer-making.
Not grazed.
Great Escarpment; Upper and Great Karoo and Orange Free State in rocky flats
and rante in very sparse vegetation.

4 **Anacampseros albidiflora**   boesmansuring, haasballetjies   **
Rounded, hairy, succulent up to 4 cm. Usually found growing in shelter of rocks
and bushes. Individual flowers on a stalk of up to 10 cm. Grazed by small herbivores.
Great Escarpment; Great and Little Karoo in stony soils on apron veld and rante.

5 **Anacampseros lanceolata**   boesmansuring, haaskos   **
Small succulent reaching 3 cm. Pink flowers on ends of 6 cm stalks. This is a
Bushman 'veldkos', but is not grazed by domestic animals.
Namaqualand; Great Escarpment; Tanqua Karoo in rante and crowns in dense
vegetation.

6 **Talinum caffrum**   osbossie   **
Soft-stemmed plant up to 30 cm, or prostrate if not supported. Flowers a rich yellow and usually closed by midday. Used medicinally by some Blacks. Only slightly
grazed.
Widespread in summer rainfall areas in flats, apron veld and rante.

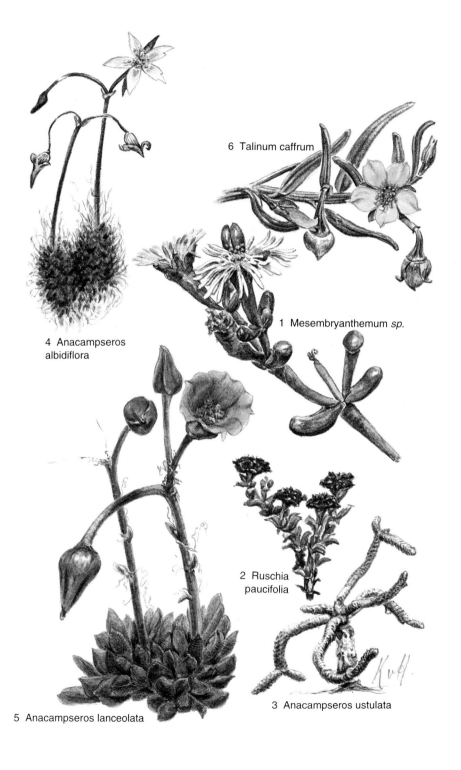

6 Talinum caffrum

4 Anacampseros
albidiflora

1 Mesembryanthemum *sp.*

2 Ruschia
paucifolia

3 Anacampseros ustulata

5 Anacampseros lanceolata

PORTULACACEAE
1 Portulacaria afra spekboom   ****
Small tree or large shrub up to 3,5 m. Stems soft. Leaves fleshy and opposite. Flowers pink and clustered. Fruit winged. Very common in some places, though much more so in days past before overgrazing almost exterminated it in some areas. Tolerates only light frosts. Leaves have been used for snuff when dry, and also to increase flow of mother's milk. Plants that grow on an eastern or northern aspect are sweet and very well grazed, while those on southerly or westerly aspects, or on shale are sour and not well grazed. Both types are botanically the same.
    Great Escarpment; Great Karoo; eastern Cape; Natal and Transvaal in apron veld, mountain slopes, and crowns.

CARYOPHYLLACEAE
2 Dianthus micropetalus wild pink, grashout, wilde-angelier   ***
Small shrub up to 7 cm. Grasslike leaves densely bunched at base. Pink or white flower closely resembles a small carnation and is borne on a stalk of up to 15 cm long. Widely used medicinally. Well grazed.
    Widespread in summer rainfall areas in rante.

3 Dianthus thunbergii wild pink, grashout, wilde-angelier   ***
Much resembles *Dianthus micropetalus* except that leaves can reach 15 cm. Well grazed.
    Great Escarpment; Great and Little Karoo; southern and eastern Cape and Transvaal in rante and mountain slopes.

ILLECEBRACEAE
4 Pollichia campestris waxberry plant, teesuikerkaroo   ****
Shrub with many stems. Leaves whorled and variable in size as shown in the illustration. Waxy-white parts of the flower resemble white to brown mulberries, are juicy and sweet, and during the Great Trek the Boers crushed them, crystallized them and then used them for sweetening. Used medicinally by many Blacks. Well grazed.
    Widespread throughout Africa in seasonal and permanent streams and a wide range of habitats.

RANUNCULACEAE
5 Clematis brachiata traveller's joy, klimop, roosmaryn   **
Rambler often covering a large shrub. In habit, foliage and flowers it resembles the British *Clematis vitalba* or traveller's joy. Widely used medicinally. Hardly grazed.
    Widespread in southern Africa on mountain slopes, wet or damp kloof and crowns.

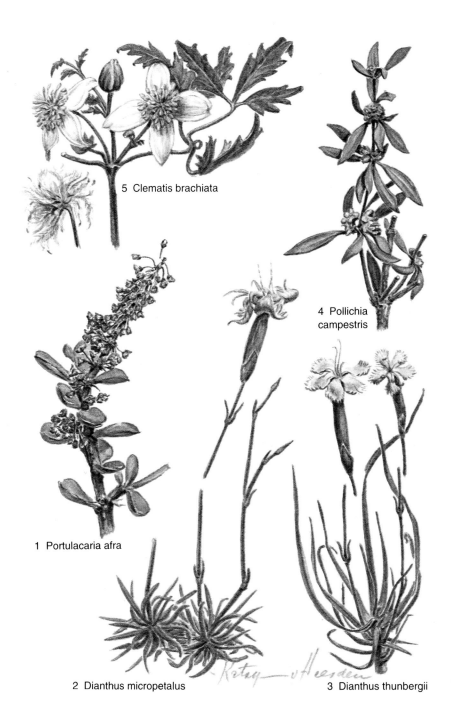

5 Clematis brachiata

4 Pollichia campestris

1 Portulacaria afra

2 Dianthus micropetalus

3 Dianthus thunbergii

RANUNCULACEAE
1 Ranunculus multifidus   buttercup, botterblom, brandblare   ★★
Semi-aquatic herb appears to be stemless with a rosette of hairy leaves arising from the long, tough, fibrous roots. Flowers solitary and a rich, yellow colour. Widely used medicinally, especially for treating cancer. Reputedly poisonous to livestock, but usually well grazed.
Widespread in Africa in permanent streams.

MENISPERMACEAE
2 Cissampelos capensis   dawidjieswortel, fynblaarklimop   ★★★★
[=Antizoma capensis]
Shrubby climber. Leaves alternate and almost triangular. Fine hairs often cover the clustered inflorescence. A well-known and much-used medicinal plant, especially as a diarrhoea cure. Very well grazed.
Widespread throughout southern Africa in seasonal streams, apron veld, rante and mountain slopes.

PAPAVERACEAE
3 Argemone ochroleuca   Mexican poppy, bloudissel   ★
[=Argemone subfusiformis]
Annual exotic herb up to 60 cm introduced from South America. Deeply lobed leaves each end in a sharp spine. Pale yellow flowers have calyx lobes with spiny margins. Rest of plant is an all over bluish colour. A related species, *Argemone mexicana*, has deeper yellow flowers, but is otherwise almost identical, and occurs only in Natal. Both species are poisonous, and people have died from eating wheat contaminated by seed. Deaths have also been reported in smallstock after grazing these plants, though this is often caused by inhaling the small spines while grazing other plants.
Widespread in southern Africa mainly in seasonal streams and disturbed areas.

4 Papaver aculeatum   thorny poppy, doringpapawer, koringroos   ★★
Annual up to 45 cm. Stems and leaves covered with stiff yellowish hairs and thorns. Flowers vary from salmon to orange-red. The only native species of this genus, it was introduced to Australia where it is regarded as good fodder. Grazed, though there is some suspicion that it may be toxic.
Widespread in southern Africa in disturbed areas.

BRASSICACEAE
5 Heliophila carnosa   blompeperbossie   ★★
Herb up to 25 cm. Rootstock woody. Alternate leaves crowded at apex of short stems. Flowers in inflorescences. Seed contained in flattened fruits that look like pods. Grazed.
Throughout the Karoo; eastern Cape; Transvaal and Namibia in flats, apron veld and rante.

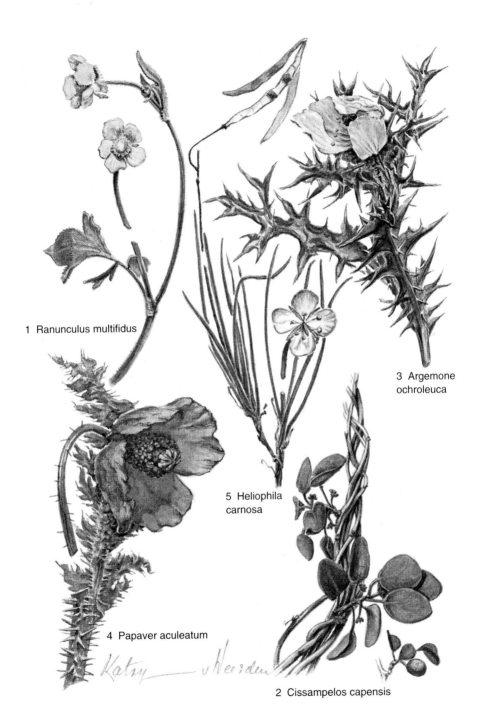

1 Ranunculus multifidus

3 Argemone ochroleuca

5 Heliophila carnosa

4 Papaver aculeatum

2 Cissampelos capensis

BRASSICACEAE
1 **Heliophila suavissima**   bloubekkie   ***
Shrub up to 60 cm. Leaves longish, narrow and often alternate or in clusters. Blue or purple flowers solitary. Seed a longish fruit. Drought resistance fair to good, and it responds to rain quickly. Well grazed, but does not supply much feed.

Throughout the Karoo; southern and eastern Cape; Natal and Orange Free State in apron veld, rante, mountain slopes and crowns.

CAPPARACEAE
2 **Cadaba aphylla**   swartstorm   **
Many-branched shrub up to 2 m. Appears to be leafless and has many stiff, blue-green shoots protruding in all directions from older stems. Flowers, which are borne in summer, vary from deep red to yellow. Seed in long, sticky fruits. Very few young plants ever seen. Some authorities consider it poisonous, but this has not yet been proven. A drawing poultice is made from finely ground stems placed between layers of gauze. A local superstition states that burning wood from this plant will make the wind blow. Very drought resistant, but hardly grazed.

Throughout arid summer rainfall areas in Tropical and southern Africa, southern and eastern Cape in seasonal streams, flats, apron veld, rante, mountain slopes and kloofs.

CRASSULACEAE
3 **Cotyledon orbiculata**   pig's ears, plakkie, kouterie   *
Succulent up to 60 cm. Different varieties have leaves varying from round to oblong and even finger-like. Inflorescences borne on long stalks with individual flowers being coral pink or yellow. Widely used medicinally, particularly to treat hard corns and warts. In days past Khoi would eat leaves after consuming meat from an animal that had died of anthrax. Not normally grazed, and has been blamed for deaths among animals. This is often, though not always, due to other *Cotyledon* species.

Widespread in southern Africa in a wide range of habitats.

4 **Tylecodon wallichii**   Wallich cotyledon, krimpsiektebos, nenta   *
A member of the Crassula family up to almost 1 m. Small protuberances where leaves had previously broken or fallen off cover its stems. Leaves longish, round in section and bunched on ends of stems. Inflorescence on a long stem, with individual flowers being yellow. Has been used medicinally by the Khoi. Animals develop 'krimpsiekte' and die in large numbers after grazing it. Dogs eating meat from a poisoned animal also developed `krimpsiekte' symptoms.

Namaqualand; Bushmanland; Great Escarpment; Northern, Upper, Great, Tanqua and Little Karoo; Cape Fold Belt; southwestern Cape and Namibia in flats, apron veld, rante and mountain slopes.

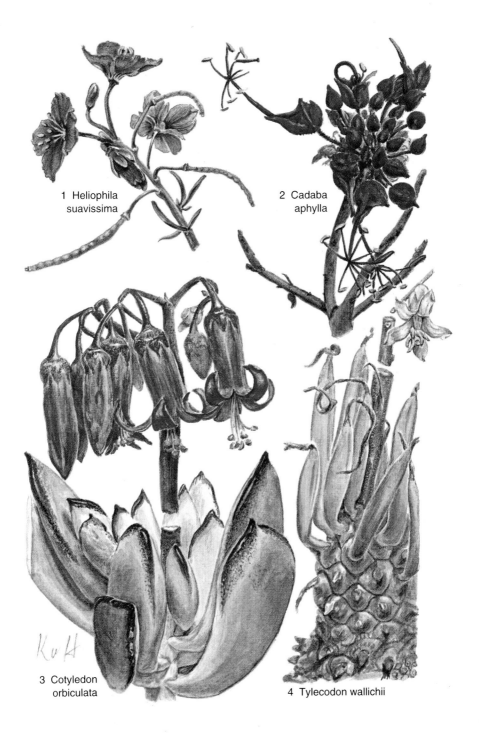

1 Heliophila
 suavissima

2 Cadaba
 aphylla

3 Cotyledon
 orbiculata

4 Tylecodon wallichii

CRASSULACEAE

1 Adromischus sphenophyllus   pig's ears, kleinplakkie, eendjie   **

Small succulent seldom exceeding 25 cm. Leaves fleshy with russet-red markings. Inflorescence on a stalk, while individual flowers are pink, tubular and very small. Usually grows inside other bushes. Not grazed.

Great Escarpment; Great and Little Karoo; southern and eastern Cape in apron veld, rante and mountain slopes.

2 Crassula montana   **

Small prostrate succulent reaching 25 mm. Can be most striking in early summer when in flower. Leaves form a small diamond. Inflorescence on a stalk about 8 cm long with white flowers. Not grazed.

Great Escarpment; Upper, Great and Little Karoo and Cape Fold Belt on mountain slopes and crowns, usually below large boulders or else clinging to rock faces.

3 Crassula muscosa var. **muscosa**   lizard's tail, skoenveterbos   ***

[=Crassula lycopodioides]

Small succulent somewhat resembling a shoelace. Varies in length, but may reach 20 cm. Stem densely packed with small, succulent leaves arranged symmetrically. Increases fast if animals are excluded from the veld, proving that it is grazed fairly readily.

Common in most arid areas of southern Africa in a wide range of habitats.

4 Crassula pyramidalis   rygbossie, koesnaatjie   **

An interesting succulent that is common locally. Leaves almost triangular in four precise ranks forming a quadrangular column. Has a mass of pink and white or off-white flowers, which unfortunately precede its death. Not grazed to any extent.

Great Escarpment; Great, Tanqua and Little Karoo in flats, apron veld, rante and mountain slopes.

5 Crassula subaphylla   louhout   ***

Shrub up to 35 cm. Succulent, oval leaves are opposite and fall off very easily, especially when it starts to get dry. Inflorescence appears on end of a blackish branch. Individual flowers minute. Locals chew it to this day for upset stomachs and abdominal pains. Well grazed and increases fast in spared veld.

Throughout the Karoo; southwestern and southern Cape and Namibia in flats, apron veld, rante and mountain slopes.

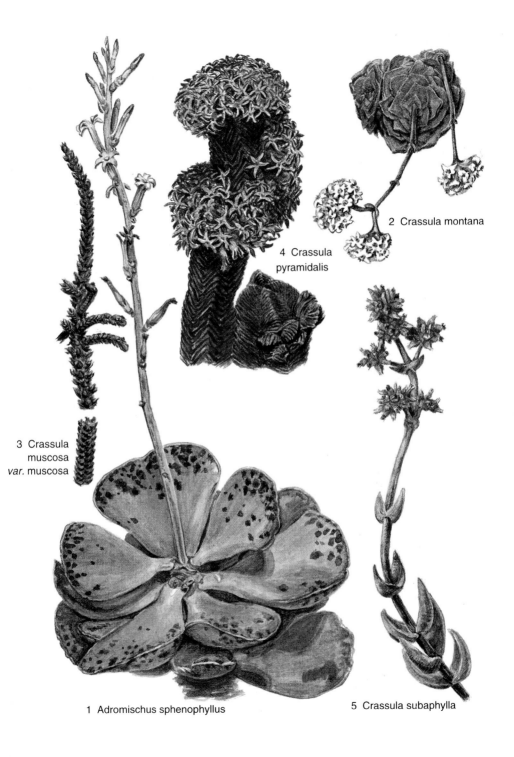

3 Crassula
muscosa
var. muscosa

4 Crassula
pyramidalis

2 Crassula montana

1 Adromischus sphenophyllus

5 Crassula subaphylla

CRASSULACEAE
1 **Crassula deltoidea**   kata-kisu   ***
Small succulent up to 12 cm. Fleshy leaves are ashy-grey. Inflorescence contains small white to pink flowers. Common name is an old San name. Readily grazed.
Throughout the Karoo; southwestern, southern and eastern Cape and Namibia in flats, apron veld and rante.

2 **Crassula rupestris**   concertina plant, sosatiebos   **
A very variable succulent. Not grazed.
Namaqualand; Great Escarpment; Great, Tanqua and Little Karoo; Cape Fold Belt; southwestern, southern and eastern Cape and Namibia on northern slopes and rante.

ROSACEAE
3 **Cliffortia arborea**   sterboom   **
Tree usually between 2 and 5 m, though sometimes reaching 10 m. Aromatic bark is grey with reddish strips flaking off. Leaves needle-like, about 2 cm long and arranged in starshaped spirals. It is the largest member of the *Cliffortia* genus. Not common. Not grazed.
Great Escarpment and Upper Karoo in kloofs and crowns, only on high mountains around Calvinia, Sutherland, Fraserburg and Beaufort West.

4 **Rubus ludwigii**   bramble, braam   **
Scrambling shrub up to just over 1 m. All parts are covered with a multitude of very sharp, hooked spines. Branches are reddish. Young twigs and the undersides of leaves are covered with down. Fruits resemble the garden raspberry, and are readily eaten. Used medicinally, and leaves are used as a tea substitute. Not grazed.
Great Escarpment; Upper Karoo and eastern Cape on crowns.

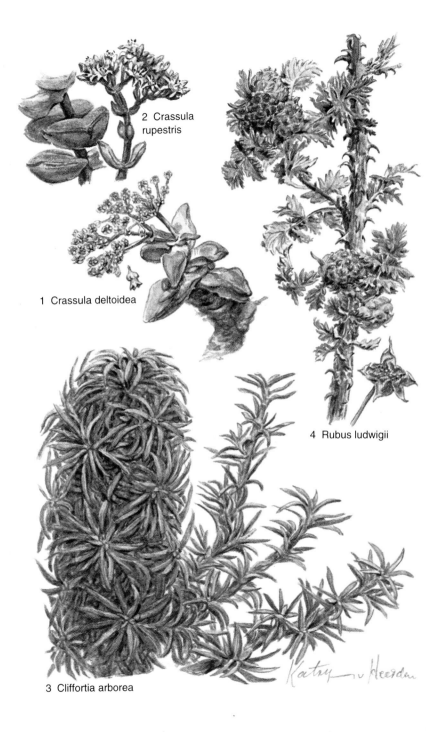

2 Crassula
rupestris

1 Crassula deltoidea

4 Rubus ludwigii

3 Cliffortia arborea

FABACEAE

1 Acacia karroo   sweet thorn, Karoo thorn, soetdoringboom ****

Deciduous tree up to 10 m. Leaves compound. Inflorescences round, yellow balls on fairly long stems that appear in early summer. Sickle-shaped seedpods may remain on the tree till midwinter. Very widespread, and possibly the best-known tree in the country. Fine specimens found in deep soil where there is enough moisture. Gum used as gum-arabic and also as sugar for cooking. Bark used for tanning leather, while seed was a coffee substitute. Wood regarded as possibly the best for 'braai-ing' in the country. A declared invader in parts of the country. Smallstock graze leaves, flowers, seed and new, young shoots readily.

Widespread throughout southern and tropical Africa in a wide range of habitats, including permanent and seasonal streams.

2 Argyrolobium collinum ***

Dwarf shrub up to 35 cm. Has an all over silvery appearance. Well grazed.

Great and Little Karoo; southern and eastern Cape in seasonal streams, flats and disturbed areas.

3 Dichilus gracilis ***

Herb up to 30 cm. Often grows inside other bushes for protection. Leaves trifoliate. Yellow flowers pea-shaped. Seedpods up to 4,5 cm. Well grazed.

Great Escarpment; Upper and Little Karoo; Eastern Cape; Orange Free State in mountain slopes and kloofs.

4 Melolobium candicans   heuningbos, stroopbos **

Shrub up to 80 cm. Many intertwined, slender branches. Small green leaves. Small yellow flowers. Lots of sharp spines throughout whole plant. Flowers rich in nectar, and attractive to bees. Not grazed, though previously suspected of poisoning livestock.

Widespread throughout the Karoo; Eastern Cape and Namibia in seasonal streams, flats, apron veld and disturbed areas.

5 Prosopis glandulosa   mesquite, suidwesdoring *

Exotic tree from southwestern United States of America up to 5 m. Has made great inroads into veld on certain farms. Feathery leaflets. Striking yellow inflorescens, flowers each with only ten stamens. Seed contained in a long pod. Highly recommended by the Department of Agriculture as a fodder tree previously, and planted throughout the Karoo. Has since run wild and taken over large areas. Now an invasive plant with farmers combatting it vigorously. A seed-feeding beetle, *Algarobius prosopis*, has recently been made available for combatting this tree. Pods well grazed by stock. Cattle take them the best, though smallstock also eat some.

Throughout the Karoo. Botswana. Namibia in permanent and seasonal streams and a wide range of habitats.

2 Argyrolobium collinum

4 Melolobium candicans

3 Dichilus gracilis

5 Prosopis glandulosa

1 Acacia karroo

FABACEAE

1 Indigofera alternans skaap-ertjie   ***
Small, prostrate annual, spreading to 30 cm. Fine hairs cover long stems. Leaves alternate, heart-shaped, light-green above, grey-green below and covered with hairs on both surfaces. Inflorescence with flowers varying from pink to deep red. Seed a pod. Some Black people eat it as a vegetable. Well grazed. Widespread throughout southern Africa in flats, apron veld and mountain slopes.

2 Indigastrum argyraeum seeroogbossie   ***
[=Indigofera argyraea, Indigofera collina]
Prostrate mat-forming perennial. Silvery-grey, hairy, trifoliate leaves form a dense crown. Pink flowers occur in short inflorescences. Has been used in a decoction to treat sore eyes. Fairly well grazed.
Throughout southern Africa in rante, mountain slopes and disturbed areas.

3 Indigofera pungens drieblaarbos   **
Shrub up to 50 cm. Many slender, dark brown stems and small dark green leaves. Single pea-shaped flowers deep red. Seed in a pod. Reasonably grazed.
Namaqualand; Great Escarpment; Great, Tanqua and Little Karoo and Namibia in rante and mountain slopes.

4 Lotononis azureoides   **
Herb up to 25 cm. Trifoliate. Flowers pea-like. A rare species found only in the Karoo National Park. Well grazed, but does not provide much fodder.
Great Escarpment on crowns.

5 Lotononis tenella   **
Small annual herb up to 25 cm. Leaves oval. Light yellow flowers pea-like. Flattened, straight pods. Well grazed when available, but does not provide any quantity of feed. Great Escarpment; Northern, Upper and Great Karoo; Cape Fold Belt; southern and eastern Cape in rante.

6 Lotononis laxa   **
Herb rarely exceeding 30 cm. Well grazed, but does not provide much fodder.
Great Escarpment; Upper Karoo; eastern Cape and Namibia on crowns.

7 Lebeckia spinescens sandganna   ****
Low-growing shrub seldom exceeding 40 cm. Hard woody base, with grey-green leaves covering new growth. Seed in a pod. Very well grazed, and is regarded as almost as good as 'ganna'. Namaqualand; Bushmanland; Great Escarpment; Northern, Upper and Great Karoo; southwestern and southern Cape in flats.

8 Medicago laciniata burr clover, klitsklawer   **
Annual herb. Trifoliate. Small yellow flowers. Spirally coiled pods or burrs have double rows of hooked spines. A native of the Mediterranean vicinity, it was introduced to the Cape in the early 1700's. Grows in winter. An important component of cultivated pastures. Burrs are troublesome in wool and mohair. Well grazed. Namaqualand; Great Escarpment; Upper, Great and Little Karoo; Cape Fold Belt; northern, southwestern and southern Cape; Orange Free State; Natal; Transvaal; Lesotho; Botswana and Namibia in disturbed areas.

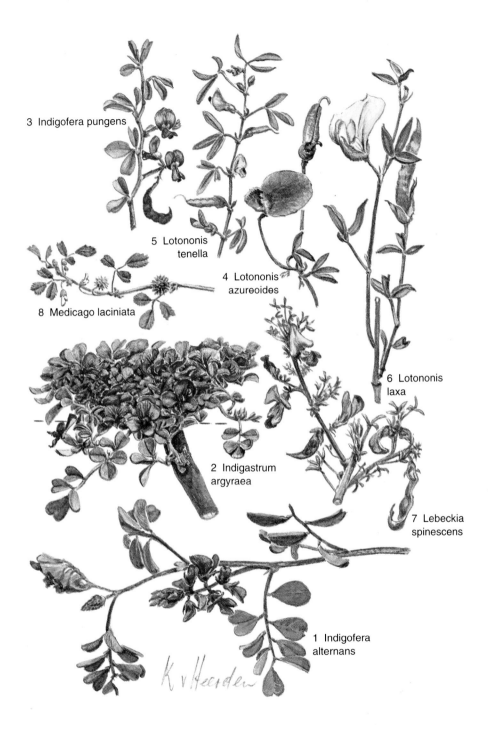

3 Indigofera pungens

5 Lotononis tenella

4 Lotononis azureoides

8 Medicago laciniata

6 Lotononis laxa

2 Indigastrum argyraea

7 Lebeckia spinescens

1 Indigofera alternans

K v Heerden

FABACEAE

1 Indigofera meyeriana   **

[=Indigofera cardiophylla]

Shrub resembling *Lotononis tenella* except that it has pink flowers. Fairly well grazed.

Bushmanland; Great Escarpment; Upper, Great and Little Karoo; southwestern and southern Cape on rante, mountain slopes and crowns.

2 Lessertia inflata   seeroogbossie   ***

Shrub up to 50 cm. Leaves grey-green. Pink flowers pea-like. Small oval pods contain seed. Often grows in sandy soils. Well grazed.

Bushmanland; Great Escarpment; Upper, Great, Tanqua and Little Karoo in seasonal streams, flats and disturbed areas.

3 Melilotus indica   yellow sweet clover, bitterklawer, stinkklawer   **

Annual exotic originating from Europe. Has strong scent. Alternate leaves have three small leaflets. Small yellow flowers. Seed contained in small oval pods. Regarded as excellent green manure. Imparts bitter taste to milk when grazed in quantity.

Widespread throughout southern Africa in disturbed areas.

4 Sutherlandia frutescens   wildekeur, kankerbos, hoenderkloek   *****

Semi-prostrate shrub to 1 m. Branches long and slender. Leaves feathery. Pea-like flowers dark pink. Seed contained in a balloon-like pod that is less than four times as long as it is wide. Very widely used medicinally, especially for the treatment of chickenpox and cancer. Very well grazed, but when taken in quantity turns milk bitter.

Widespread in southern Africa on flats, apron veld, rante and disturbed areas.

5 Sutherlandia microphylla   kankerbos, bitterblaar, hoenderkloek   *****

Shrub much the same as *Sutherlandia frutescens* except that it is more erect. Grows to 2 m. Pods more than four times as long as wide. Used medicinally for washing wounds, fevers, chickenpox and cancer. Very well grazed, but makes milk bitter when taken in quantity.

Widespread in southern Africa in seasonal streams, flats and disturbed areas.

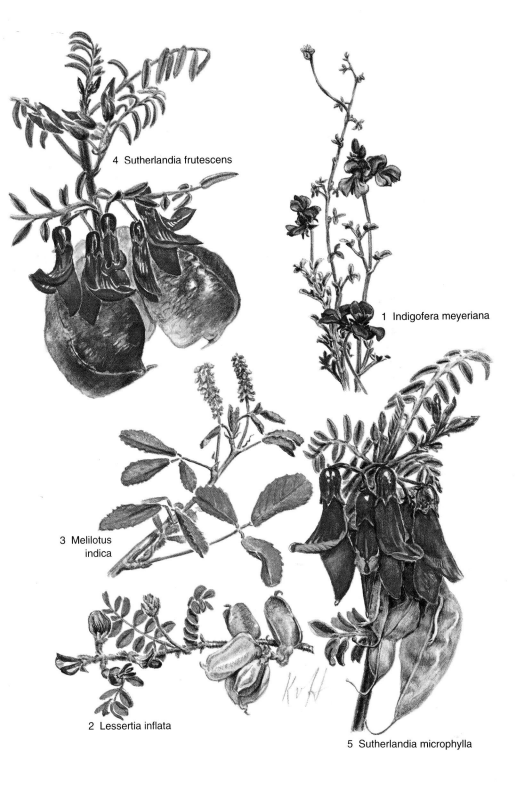

4 Sutherlandia frutescens

1 Indigofera meyeriana

3 Melilotus indica

2 Lessertia inflata

5 Sutherlandia microphylla

GERANIACEAE

1 **Pelargonium alternans** blomkoolmalva   ***
Shrub up to 35 cm. Leaves cover the plant and hide the somewhat untidy stems from view. Well grazed.

Great Escarpment; Great, Tanqua and Little Karoo in rante and mountain slopes, usually in rocky situations, often in dolerite.

2 **Pelargonium grossularioides** rooirabasam   **
Aromatic herb up to 30 cm. Reddish stems hairy. Leaves deeply lobed. Inflorescence in an umbrella shape. San used a decoction to procure abortions and help with confinements. Not grazed.

Widespread in southern Africa in flood plains, wet or damp kloofs and disturbed areas.

3 **Pelargonium multicaule**   **
Dwarf shrub seldom exceeding 30 cm. Not much grazed.

Great Escarpment; Upper and Little Karoo; southwestern and eastern Cape and Lesotho on mountain slopes and crowns.

4 **Pelargonium abrotanifolium**   **
Shrub up to 30 cm. Grazed to a limited extent.

Namaqualand; Great Escarpment; Northern, Great Karoo and Orange Free State in rante, mountain slopes, kloofs and crowns.

5 **Pelargonium tetragonum**   **
Erect shrub reaching 2 m. Usually grows inside other plants such as *Rhigozum obovatum* and *Lycium* species for support and protection. Stems brittle. Flowers off-white and large for the Karoo. Not much grazed.

Great Escarpment; Great and Little Karoo; southern and eastern Cape and Namibia in apron veld.

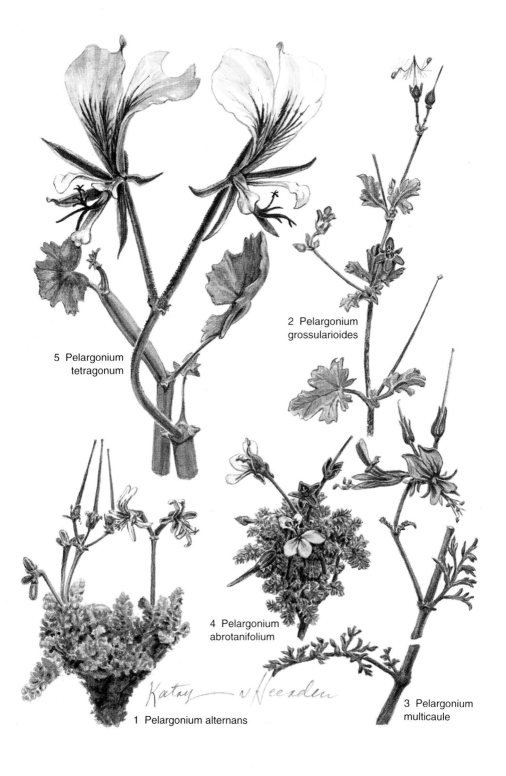

5 Pelargonium
tetragonum

2 Pelargonium
grossularioides

4 Pelargonium
abrotanifolium

3 Pelargonium
multicaule

1 Pelargonium alternans

Katay —— v Heeaden

GERANIACEAE
1 **Pelargonium glutinosum**   **
Herb seldom exceeding 35 cm. Not much grazed.
Great Escarpment; Upper, Great and Little Karoo; Cape Fold Belt; southwestern and southern Cape on mountain slopes, kloofs and crowns.

2 **Pelargonium** sp.   **
Shrub reaching 15 cm. Not grazed.
Nieuweveld mountains and Drakensberg of Natal and Lesotho on crowns, frequenting high, cold and dry areas.

3 **Pelargonium exhibens**   **
Shrub seldom exceeding 35 cm. Has a slight scent. Bright green leaves very deeply incised. Stems dotted with very fine hairs. Hardly grazed.
Great escarpment in kloofs and mountain slopes. Found mainly near Beaufort West, Graaff-Reinet and Grahamstown.

4 **Sarcocaulon camdeboense**   kersbos   **
Shrub with succulent stems reaching 20 cm with a spread of 40 cm. Flowers a very light yellow. Not grazed.
Great Escarpment; Upper and Great Karoo in flats and rante.

5 **Sarcocaulon crassicaule**   candlebush, grootkersbos   **
Shrub with succulent stems up to 75 cm. Thick stems, covered with spines, contain large quantities of resin making them inflammable even when green. Leaves oval. Single flowers white to pale yellow. Torches made from the stems used to burn spines off prickly pears. Not grazed.
Namaqualand; Bushmanland; Great Escarpment; Northern, Upper, Great and Little Karoo; southwestern and southern Cape and Namibia in flats, rante and mountain slopes.

6 **Sarcocaulon salmoniflorum**   bushman's candle, kleinkersbossie   **
Resembles *Sarcocaulon camdeboense* except that flowers are salmon pink. Not grazed.
Namaqualand; Bushmanland; Great Escarpment; Northern, Upper, Great, Tanqua and Little Karoo; southern and northern Cape; Orange Free State and Namibia in flats.

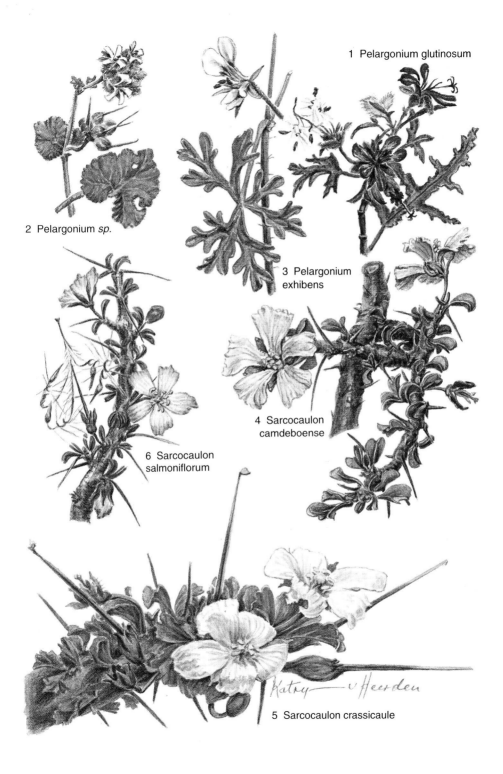

1 Pelargonium glutinosum

2 Pelargonium *sp.*

3 Pelargonium exhibens

4 Sarcocaulon camdeboense

6 Sarcocaulon salmoniflorum

5 Sarcocaulon crassicaule

GERANIACEAE

1 **Erodium cicutarium**   horlosiewysterbos, muskuskruid   **
Herb, originating in Europe, forms small mats up to 20 cm in diameter. Inflorescence with small purple flowers. Fruit shaped like a rapier. Has a musk-like odour. Fairly well grazed.
Widespread in the Cape and Lesotho in moist disturbed areas.

2 **Pelargonium karooicum**   **
Straggly shrub not exceeding 35 cm. Often found inside other larger bushes that provide support and protection. Flowers a delicate white with red dots. Only a few leaves on long, brittle stems. Reasonably grazed, but cannot supply much feed.
Great Escarpment; Great, Tanqua and Little Karoo and southwestern Cape in rante.

3 **Pelargonium articulatum**   **
Semi-geophyte, sometimes summer deciduous with an underground rhizome consisting of alternating thick and thin portions. Leaves directly from the rhizome, dark green and often with a darker zone. Grazed to a limited degree.
Namaqualand; Great Escarpment; Great Karoo and southwestern Cape on mountain slopes, kloofs and crowns.

4 **Pelargonium griseum**   dassie buchu, dassiebos, sinkingsbos   **
Densely branched shrub up to 45 cm. Leaves scented. Inflorescence with white to pink individual flowers. Infusion of leaves used for gout, rheumatism and colds in Sutherland. Only slightly grazed.
Great Escarpment in rante and mountain slopes.

OXALIDACEAE

5 **Oxalis commutata**   sorrel, suring   **
Small herb appearing in flats after good spring rains. Not much grazed as there are many other more palatable plants available when it is growing.
Widespread in southern and tropical Africa in a wide range of habitats.

6 **Oxalis pes-caprae**   wood sorrel, yellow oxalis, geelsuring   **
Small cormous herb up to 35 cm. Flower yellow. Leaves trifoliate. Insect repellent is made from corms, while sap from the crushed plant is used to remove ink stains. Has a pleasant taste, and adults and children alike chew it. A weed in Australia and California. There have been unconfirmed reports of deaths from chewing too many, also reports of animals dying from oxalic acid poisoning after grazing on them.
Now cosmopolitan in a wide range of habitats.

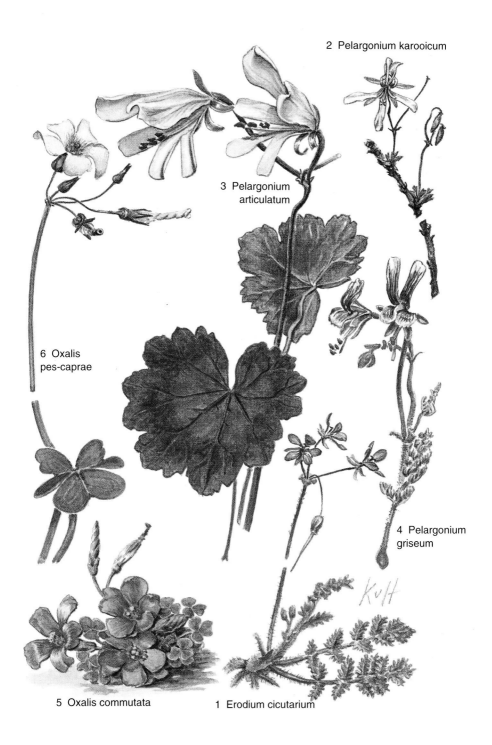

2 Pelargonium karooicum

3 Pelargonium articulatum

6 Oxalis pes-caprae

4 Pelargonium griseum

5 Oxalis commutata

1 Erodium cicutarium

ZYGOPHYLLACEAE
1 **Augea capensis** bobbejaankos, kinderpiel   **
Shrub up to 50 cm. Leaves succulent. Roots full of moisture. Black people may insult one another by referring to this plant as the other's food. Not usually grazed as leaves are very saline. During droughts baboons may dig up roots and small-stock may eat some seed. Ostriches appear to like it.
Namaqualand; Bushmanland; Great, Tanqua and Little Karoo and Namibia in flats and disturbed areas.

2 **Tribulus terrestris** devil's thorn, dubbeltjiedoring, dubbeltjie   * or ***
Prostrate annual. Branches reach 1 m in good conditions. Pinnate leaves opposite. Flowers yellow. Spiny fruits have 3 to 5 fused carpels. It may be exotic as it is cosmopolitan today. Used medicinally as a tonic, for diarrhoea and diseases of throat and eyes. Well grazed, but under certain conditions causes 'geeldikkop', or photosensitization, in sheep and goats. First reported in 1899. In 1926-27 ±600,000 sheep died of this disease.
Widespread throughout southern Africa in flood plains, flats and disturbed areas.

3 **Zygophyllum incrustatum** skeleton bush, witkriedoring   **
Shrub up to 50 cm. White stems. Usually only a few bright green, almost round leaves that fall off easily. Yellow flowers. In a drought they look like dried-out, white skeletons. Hardly grazed.
Bushmanland; Northern, Upper and Great Karoo and Orange Free State in flats.

4 **Zygophyllum lichtensteinianum** skilpadbos, vaalspekbos   ***
Much-branched shrub to 75 cm. Branches grow in all directions. Leaflets almost round and fall off easily, particularly when it gets dry. Flowers yellow, and cover plant after rains. Seed 4-winged. Very drought-resistant and sought-after by all types of smallstock. Some of its value disappears during a drought when leaves fall off, but it recovers well after rain.
Bushmanland; Great Escarpment; Northern, Tanqua, Upper and Great Karoo; northern and southern Cape and Orange Free State in seasonal streams, flats and rante.

5 **Zygophyllum microcarpum** ouooibos   * or **
Rigid shrub up to 1 m. Stems light. Flowers pale yellow. Seed 4-winged. Grazed to some extent, but can cause very heavy losses in sheep if they graze as much as 500 g. Causes anaemia, hemorrhaging of lymph glands, hyperaemia of inner organs and enteritis. Stock used to veld where it occurs often avoid it, though revert to it when grazing dries off.
Bushmanland; Northern and Upper Karoo; Great Escarpment; Great Karoo; Orange Free State and Namibia in seasonal streams, flood plains and flats.

6 **Zygophyllum retrofractum** hondepisbos, jakkalsbos   **
Much-branched shrub to 60 cm. Very small leaves vary from light green through grey, brown to almost red in cold weather. Flowers insignificant. Winged seed produced in great abundance at first glance resemble small brown fruit, but are 5 seeds fused together. Increases in over-grazed areas. Not grazed. Namaqualand; Bushmanland; Great Escarpment; Great and Tanqua Karoo; southwestern and southern Cape and Namibia in seasonal streams, flats, rante and disturbed areas.

90

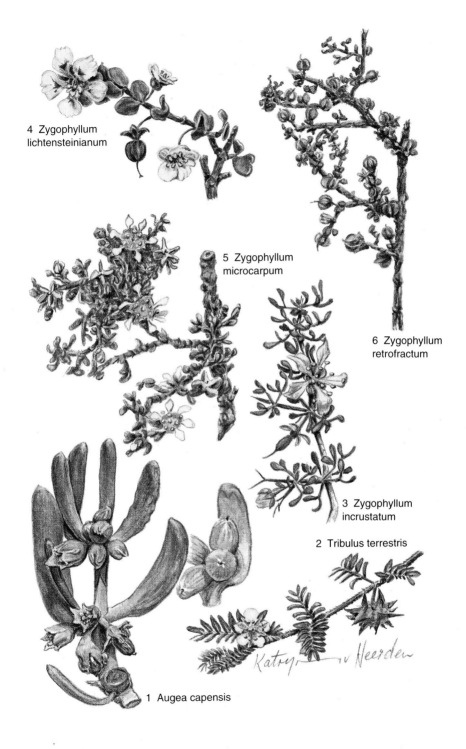

4 Zygophyllum
lichtensteinianum

5 Zygophyllum
microcarpum

6 Zygophyllum
retrofractum

3 Zygophyllum
incrustatum

2 Tribulus terrestris

1 Augea capensis

Katry v Heerden

POLYGALACEAE

1 Muraltia macrocarpa   **

Shrub up to 1 m. Leaves narrow. Solitary flowers white or pink. Hardly grazed.
Great Escarpment; Great and Little Karoo; Cape Fold Belt; southwestern and eastern Cape in rante and mountain slopes.

2 Polygala asbestina   skaap-ertjie   ****

Small prostrate dwarf shrub up to 15 cm in diameter. Feathery, small, blue flowers. Very well grazed by all types of animals. Great Escarpment; Northern, Great and Little Karoo; southern and eastern Cape in rante and mountain slopes.

3 Polygala ephedroides   skaap-ertjie   ****

Straggling shrub up to 55 cm. Flower not noticeable due to greenish colour. If left to seed, it increases rapidly. Often found only inside other bushes as it is very palatable to all animals. Namaqualand; Great Escarpment; Upper, Great and Little Karoo; southwestern and southern Cape and Namibia in a wide range of habitats.

4 Polygala leptophylla   skaap-ertjie   ****

Dwarf shrub up to 30 cm. Narrow, alternate leaves. Flowers borne on leafless branches. Usually found in stony ground, often sheltered in other bushes. Drought resistant and responds well to any rain. Medicinally used to promote sweating. Very well grazed.
Namaqualand; Bushmanland; Great Escarpment; Northern, Upper and Great Karoo; northern Cape and Namibia in rante and mountain slopes.

5 Polygala bowkerae   skaap-ertjie   ***

Dwarf shrub up to 40 cm. Well grazed, but produces little feed owing to its small size. Great Escarpment and Great Karoo in rante, slopes and kloofs.

EUPHORBIACEAE

All Euphorbias produce a milky latex that can be irritating to animals when grazed.

6 Euphorbia mauritanica   geelmelkbos, gifmelkbos   *

Shrub up to 1 m. Branches round, yellow-green, erect. Small leaves opposite on tips of branches, shedding soon. Yellow flowers. Fruit with 3 compartments. Latex used by San for arrow poison, though probably mainly for its cohesive properties. Hardly grazed, causing poisoning similar to that of 'melktou' (*Sarcostemma viminale*). ie. foaming at the mouth, rapid breathing, muscular tremor and a stiff gait. Widespread throughout southern Africa in flats, apron veld, rante and mountain slopes.

7 Euphorbia stolonifera   kruipmelkbos, rankmelkbos   **

Dwarf shrub up to 50 cm. Leafless, robust stems. Flowers yellow to orange. Spreads laterally by underground stems. Hardly grazed.
Great Karoo and southern Cape in flats.

8 Euphorbia rhombifolia   **

Dense slender shrub to 75 cm. Almost leafless secondary stems do not fork. This seems to be nature's way of coping with extremes of heat and drought. Usually grows in clumps. Not grazed. Great and Little Karoo; southwestern, southern and eastern Cape and Natal in flats.

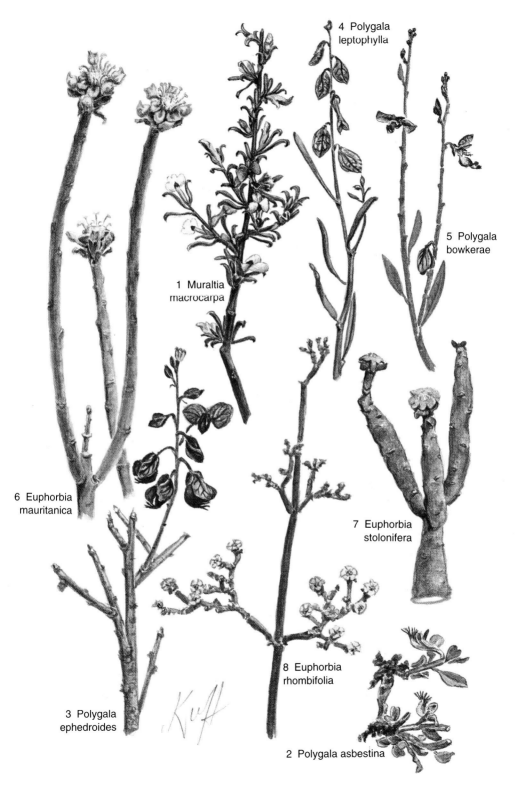

4 Polygala
leptophylla

1 Muraltia
macrocarpa

5 Polygala
bowkerae

6 Euphorbia
mauritanica

7 Euphorbia
stolonifera

8 Euphorbia
rhombifolia

3 Polygala
ephedroides

2 Polygala asbestina

EUPHORBIACEAE

1 Euphorbia braunsii   vingerpol   **
Small succulent up to 20 cm. Many short, thick branches growing from a base that hardly comes above the ground, they are covered with protuberances and exude a sticky latex if damaged. Small leaves appear in tufts on tips of branches. Flowers small and yellow. Seed in a capsule containing 3 to 4 seeds. Latex used for its cohesive properties in arrow poison by the San. Not grazed.
   Great Escarpment; Northern, Upper, Great and Little Karoo and northern Cape in flats and rante.

2 Euphorbia caterviflora   springbokmelkbos   **
One of several stemless *Euphorbia* species that may be confused with one another. Seldom grows to more than 45 cm. Branches all come from base, and this gives it a spiky appearance. Leaves minute. Green and yellow flowers small. Latex in stems an irritant, but in the quantity consumed does not appear to have any adverse effects. Grazed by sheep and goats, but cannot provide any appreciable volume to their diet.
   Great Escarpment; Great and Little Karoo and southwestern Cape in flats and rante.

3 Euphorbia stellispina   noorsdoring   **
Succulent up to 75 cm. Thick stems each have up to 16 grooves. They vary from green to grey-green and brown depending on age, and are covered with spines, which occur in a crown on tip of stem. Leaves small, but fall off very soon. Small yellow flowers appear on the tip of the stem. Usually grows on shallow, stony ground. Latex used to make bird-lime. Not grazed.
   Namaqualand; Great Escarpment and Great Karoo in rante and mountain slopes.

4 Euphorbia decepta   melkpol   **
Succulent up to 20 cm. Body of plant round with long fingers protruding. Flowers and fruit borne on fingers. Not grazed.
   Great Karoo in flats.

5 Euphorbia suffulta   **
Inconspicuous, newly described species with small paired stipules on stems like *Euphorbia burmannii*. Not grazed.
   Great Karoo on rante.

6 Euphorbia burmannii   steenbokmelkbos, lidjiesmelkbos   **
Shrub up to 70 cm. Has many branches that, when dry, break into pieces. Flowers green. Not grazed.
   Namaqualand; Great and Little Karoo; southwestern, southern and eastern Cape in varied habitats.

94

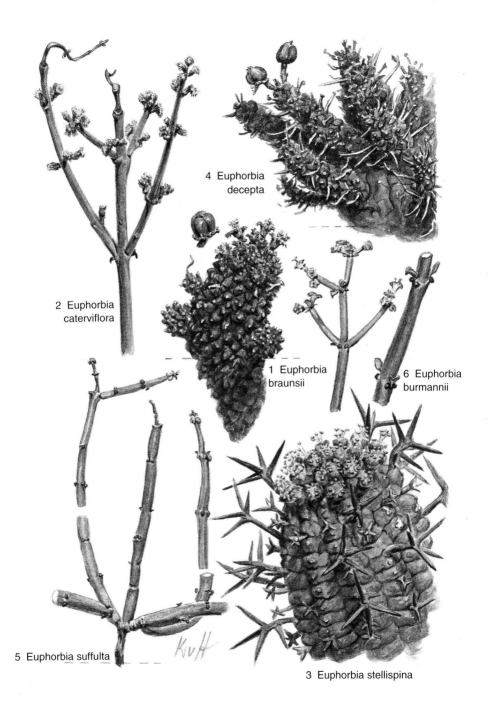

4 Euphorbia decepta

2 Euphorbia caterviflora

1 Euphorbia braunsii

6 Euphorbia burmannii

5 Euphorbia suffulta

3 Euphorbia stellispina

ANACARDIACEAE
1 Rhus burchellii   taaibos, kunibos   **

Large shrub to small tree reaching 2-3 m. On hills and mountains of the Karoo it has typically small leaves, though where it grows near watercourses leaves can grow larger. Flowers in autumn. Fruit green. Another taaibos is *Rhus undulata* that grows up to 5 m and has larger leaves. An infusion of leaves is an old Namaqua remedy for chest colds. Chewing them will give same result. A tough, drought-resistant plant whose only economic value would be the shelter it gives animals and the ground cover it provides. Not grazed.

Throughout Cape, Orange Free State; Natal; Transvaal; Lesotho and Namibia in flats, rante and mountain slopes.

2 Rhus dregeana   basterkareeboom, besembos   **

Small tree up to 1,4 m. Glabrous with small elongated leaflets. Produces masses of seed that early Khoisan ate. Later White settlers made jelly from seed. Not grazed.

Great Escarpment; Upper Karoo; eastern and northern Cape and Orange Free State on mountain slopes.

3 Rhus lancea   kareeboom, hoenderspoorkaree   **

Evergreen tree up to approximately 9 m, it stands out along river banks and scattered throughout hills and flats. Compound, trifoliate leaves with centre leaflet being longer than the other two. This gives it the common name of 'hoenderspoorkaree' (hen's foot karee). Flowers in yellow clusters cover tree in winter and early spring. Edible, brown fruit ripen in early summer. Very long-lived tree. A specimen that William Burchell camped under in 1811 was recently chopped down to make way for an electric pylon. Timber is tough and used by early settlers for furniture and a variety of other joinery. A great favorite for fencing posts. Also used for tanning as there is a considerable quantity of tannin in leaves and twigs. Hardly grazed.

Throughout Southern Africa except Natal in permanent and seasonal streams, flats and kloofs.

4 Rhus pyroides   fire thorn, brandtaaibos   **

Large shrub up to 5 m. Branches spiny. Leaves smallish. Off-white flowers appear in clusters. A prick or scratch from this plant burns like fire. Not grazed, but does provide ground cover and shelter.

Great Escarpment; Upper and Great Karoo; southern, eastern and northern Cape; Orange Free State; Natal; Transvaal and Lesotho in permanent and seasonal streams, rante, mountain slopes, kloofs and crowns.

RHAMNACEAE
5 Rhamnus prinoides   dogwood, redwood, blinkblaar, rooibos   **

Tree up to 7 m. Leaves alternate and very glossy on upper side. Small flowers yellowish-green. Fruit, about the size of peas, bright red when ripe. Locals prize the hard, white timber. A tincture made from parts of this tree have purgative properties. Not grazed.

Great Escarpment; Upper and Great Karoo; southern and eastern Cape; Orange Free State; Natal; Transvaal; Lesotho and Zimbabwe on mountain slopes and kloofs.

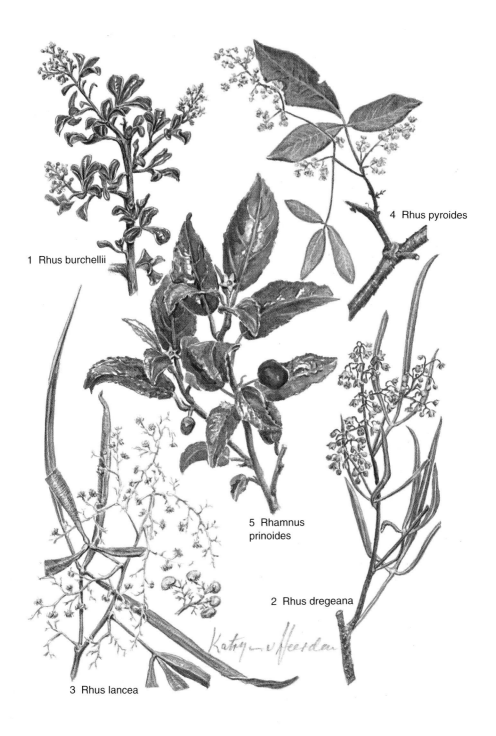

1 Rhus burchellii

4 Rhus pyroides

5 Rhamnus prinoides

2 Rhus dregeana

3 Rhus lancea

CELASTRACEAE
1 **Maytenus heterophylla**   common spike-thorn, gewone pendoring   **
Tree or shrub up to 5 m. Young branches brown, green or reddish-purple becoming grey with age. Characterized by numerous long, up to 17,5 cm thorns that can pierce a tyre. Leaves in clusters on dwarf branchlets, occasionally on green thorns. Masses of cream flowers have a strong scent. Very drought resistant. Not much grazed till conditions become dry. Goats take leaves more readily than sheep.
   Widespread throughout southern Africa in a variety of habitats.

MELIANTHACEAE
2 **Melianthus comosus**   kruidjie-roer-my-niet   *
Shrub up to 2 m. Serrated leaves, when crushed or bruised, have very strong foetid smell. Dark, orange-red flowers produce lots of nectar, attracting sunbirds and bees. Winged, inflated capsule contains round, black seeds. Those setting traps for jackal and other wild animals often use branches to obliterate their smell by brushing the ground after setting the trap. Used extensively medicinally. Not grazed by animals, but very poisonous if ingested accidentally. Mistletoe that sometimes grows on the shrub is very palatable to livestock, and, like its host, can easily kill them.
   Throughout Southern Africa except Natal in permanent and seasonal streams, flats and kloofs.

TILIACEAE
3 **Grewia robusta**   kruisbessiebos, karkarbessie   ****
Shrub up to between 2 and 3 m. Leaves alternate and their undersides and the younger branches are covered in minute hairs. Flowers pink. Small green fruit turning brown as they ripen, growing in a cross and are edible. Very eagerly grazed by all animals, so very few young plants reach maturity.
   Great Escarpment; Great and Little Karoo and eastern Cape in apron veld, rante, mountain slopes and kloofs.

MALVACEAE
4 **Anisodontea capensis**   wildestokroos   **
One of many different *Anisodontea* species. An upright shrub reaching 1,5 m. Flowers light pink. Not grazed.
   Great Escarpment on mountain slopes and kloofs

5 **Hibiscus atromarginatus**   **
A small shrub reaching 40 cm. Not grazed.
   Great Escarpment and Great Karoo in flats and crowns.

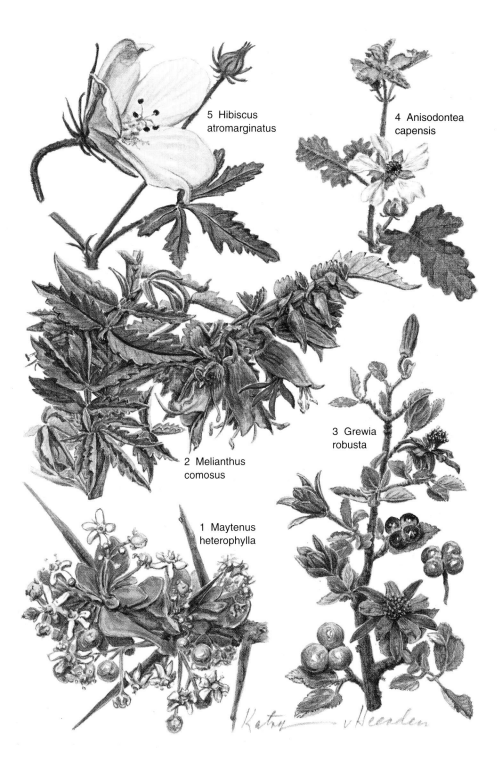

5 Hibiscus atromarginatus

4 Anisodontea capensis

2 Melianthus comosus

3 Grewia robusta

1 Maytenus heterophylla

MALVACEAE

1 **Anisodontea malvastroides** wildestokroos **

Upright shrub reaching 1,5 m. Stems grey. Leaves grey-green and covered, particularly on the underside, with a downy substance. Flowers solitary, and in two shades of pink. Hardly grazed.

Great Escarpment; Upper and Great Karoo on mountain slopes, kloofs and crowns.

2 **Anisodontea triloba** wildestokroos **

Erect shrub up to 2 m. Stems hairy, especially when young. Ovate leaves very hairy and 3-lobed. Flowers much the same as *Anisodontea scabrosa*. Often grows in veld that has been burnt. Not grazed.

Namaqualand; Great Escarpment; Upper, Great and Little Karoo and southwestern Cape in permanent and seasonal streams, rante, mountain slopes and kloofs.

3 **Hibiscus pusillus** bladderweed, Terblansbossie **

Exotic originating from Europe. Erect, annual shrub up to 1,3 m, though usually much shorter in this area. Flowers vary from cream through yellow to pink and have a dark centre. Not grazed.

Great Escarpment; Upper, Great and Little Karoo; southwestern, southern and eastern Cape; Orange Free State; Botswana, Lesotho, Namibia and Swaziland in wet kloofs.

4 **Malva parviflora** small mallow, kiesieblaar **

Weed introduced from Europe in about 1700. Strong taproot. Leaves large, lobed and have serrated margins. Flowers insignificant. Usually grow in gardens and on disturbed ground. Leaves used as a decoction for sore throats and as a poultice. Mildly poisonous, especially to horses, and can affect cattle as well, but they have to consume considerable quantities. Laying hens consuming malvaceous plants lay eggs whose whites turn pink when stored. Only slightly grazed.

Cosmopolitan in disturbed areas.

5 **Radyera urens** wildekalbas, pampoenbossie **

Prostrate herb looking like a cucurbit. Grey-green, lobed leaves have crinkled margins. Flowers deep red. Whole plant covered in hairs. Not grazed.

Namaqualand; Bushmanland; Great Escarpment; Northern, Great and Tanqua Karoo and northern Cape in flats and disturbed areas.

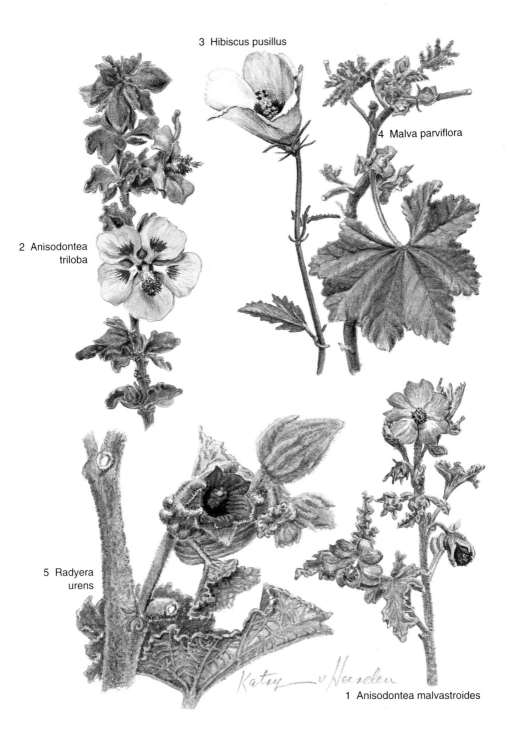

3 Hibiscus pusillus

4 Malva parviflora

2 Anisodontea
triloba

5 Radyera
urens

1 Anisodontea malvastroides

STERCULIACEAE

1 Hermannia althaefolia bokkiesblom, pokkiesblom ***
Perennial up to 50 cm. Whole plant slightly hairy. Flowers yellow. Cultivated in Europe during 18th century. Used medicinally as an aromatic tea against syphilis. Grazed.

Namaqualand; Great Escarpment; Great, Tanqua and Little Karoo; Cape Fold Belt; southwestern and southern Cape in flats, rante and crowns.

2 Hermannia cococarpa moederkappie ***
Low-growing shrub to 25 cm. Long leaves, which are coarsely serrated. Flowers variable in colour, though usually red with, very often, some white visible. Well grazed by all small stock.

Great Escarpment and eastern Cape in rante and mountain slopes.

3 Hermannia desertorum suikerbos ****
Shrub up to 30 cm. Branches closely packed together, often giving it the appearance of a ball. Yellow and orange flowers appear in summer, and resemble small, twisted bells. Seeds well and germinates easily. Many small plants survive if grazing practices allow it. Very drought-resistant. Very well grazed by all livestock.

Namaqualand; Great Escarpment; Northern, Upper and Great Karoo; Cape Fold Belt; northern Cape and Namibia in flats, apron veld and rante.

4 Hermannia grandiflora klokkiebos, ouma-se-kappie ***
Shrub reaches 40 cm. Forms a striking patch of colour when in full flower. Deeply lobed, dark green leaves. Flowers, which can cover the bush, a brilliant pink. Well grazed.

Bushmanland; Great Escarpment; Northern, Upper, Great and Little Karoo and southwestern Cape in flats, apron veld, rante and mountain slopes.

5 Hermannia johanssenii ***
Shrub up to 60 cm with overall yellowish-grey colour. Stems hairy, the older ones grey and the younger olive-green. Leaves densely covered by pale greyish hairs. Flowers yellow. Reasonably grazed.

Great Escarpment; Upper and Great Karoo in sand, clay and shales in rante.

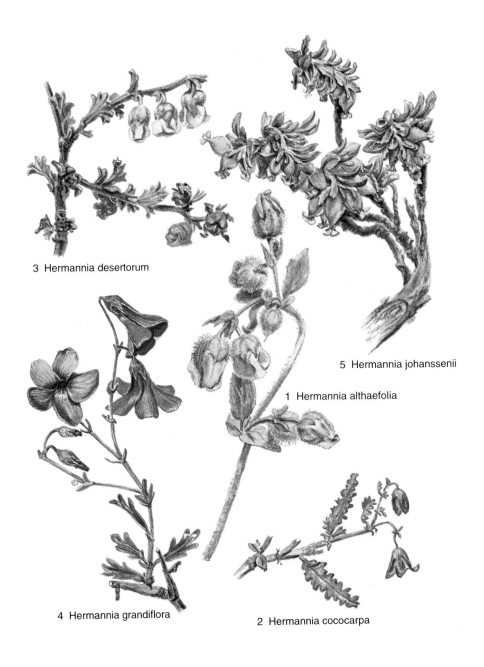

3 Hermannia desertorum

5 Hermannia johanssenii

1 Hermannia althaefolia

4 Hermannia grandiflora

2 Hermannia cococarpa

STERCULIACEAE

1 **Hermannia vestita** swaelbossie   **

Shrub reaching 30 cm. Often grows near rocks inhabited by dassies. Leaves very light green, deeply veined with crinkled edges. Flowers yellow and typical *Hermannia* form. Can form a very dense mat on a steep hillside, and thus provides a considerable amount of ground cover. Grazed only under very intensive systems.

Great Escarpment; Northern, Upper and Great Karoo; Orange Free State in rante, mountain slopes and stream banks.

2 **Hermannia cernua** subsp. **jacobeifolia**   **

Shrub to 25 cm. Only a few stems. Leaves typical of *Hermannia*. Flowers blue. Well grazed, but cannot supply much feed.

Great Escarpment; Upper and Great Karoo in seasonal streams, flood plains, flats, apron veld and disturbed areas.

3 **Hermannia cuneifolia** var. **cuneifolia** agtdaegeneesbos   ****

Aromatic shrub up to 50 cm. Leaves wedge-shaped and slightly hairy. Bright yellow to orange pendulous flowers. Used medicinally, especially as an infusion or decoction that is both applied to sores and taken internally. Drought resistant and well grazed.

Throughout the Cape and Lesotho in seasonal streams and a wide range of habitats.

4 **Hermannia filifolia** var. **grandicalyx**   ****

Fairly large shrub not exceeding 45 cm. Branches reddish and usually straight. Leaves long and narrow and occur either alternately or in tufts. Pendulous flowers orange to red. Drought resistant and responds well to even light rain. Well grazed.

Great Escarpment; Upper, Great and Little Karoo; Cape Fold Belt and southwestern Cape in flats, apron veld, rante, mountain slopes and kloofs.

5 **Hermannia pulchella** bergpleisterbos   **

Dwarf shrub to 25 cm. Leaves alternate, simple and bright green. Flowers pendulous, yellow and sweetly scented. Grows in rocky habitats. Bees work flowers. Not much grazed.

Namaqualand; Bushmanland; Great Escarpment; Upper and Great Karoo and northern Cape in rante and mountain slopes.

6 **Hermannia spinosa** steekbossie   **

Shrub up to 30 cm. Stems white with many sharp projections much resembling spines. Leaves longish. Pendulous red flowers. Hardly grazed.

Bushmanland; Great Escarpment; Northern, Upper, Great and Little Karoo and northern Cape in seasonal streams, flats, apron veld and rante.

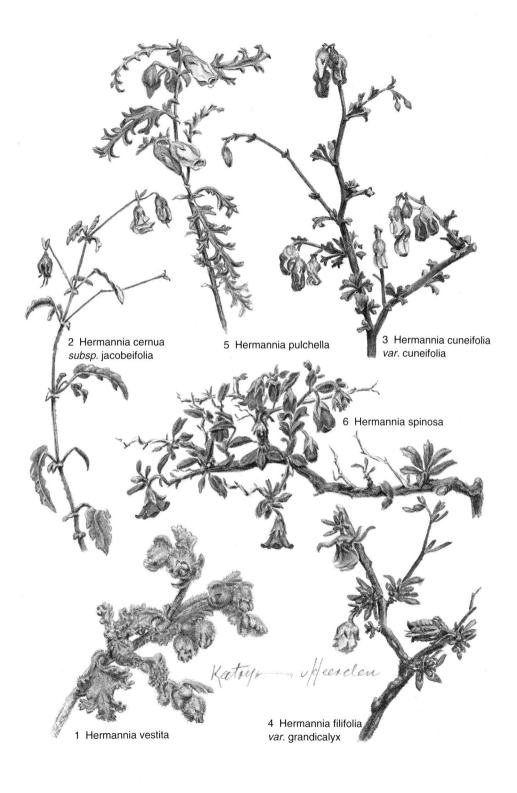

2 Hermannia cernua
subsp. jacobeifolia

5 Hermannia pulchella

3 Hermannia cuneifolia
var. cuneifolia

6 Hermannia spinosa

1 Hermannia vestita

4 Hermannia filifolia
var. grandicalyx

TAMARICACEAE
1 **Tamarix usneoides**   tamarisk, dabbie, soutboom   **

Tree up to 5 m found in groups because it suckers. Pale, grey-green leaves are sharp pointed scales that completely cover young stems. Bark brownish-grey on older stems and reddish when younger. Inflorescences on upper parts of branches. Very small flowers creamy-white to pink. The name 'dabbie' is from the original Khoekhoen. Grazed to some extent.

Namaqualand; Bushmanland; Great Escarpment; Northern, Upper and Great Karoo; Cape Fold Belt; southwestern, southern and northern Cape and Namibia in seasonal streams and flood plains.

FLACOURTIACEAE
2 **Kiggelaria africana**   wild peach, speekhout   **

Evergreen to semi-deciduous tree up to 15 m. Pale grey, smooth bark sometimes appears rusty. Flowers yellowish-green. Fruit a capsule of the same colour containing bright orange-red seed. Timber suitable for boards, furniture, and in earlier days spokes for wagon wheels. Not grazed.

Namaqualand; Great Escarpment; Northern, Great, Tanqua and Little Karoo; Cape Fold Belt; southwestern, southern, eastern and northern Cape; Transvaal; Orange Free State; Natal; Lesotho, Namibia, Swaziland and Zimbabwe in kloofs.

THYMELAEACEAE
3 **Gnidia deserticola**   t'korbos, Hotnotsverfbossie, saffraanbos   ***

Shrub up to 45 cm. Somewhat hairy leaves usually clustered near tips of branches. Yellow and orange flowers with long tubes, covered with minute hairs. Flowers make a permanent yellow dye which Burchell used for paint during his travels in 1811. Some years later the colour had still not faded. The Khoi used them to dye leather. Well grazed, especially if the stocking density is high.

Great Escarpment; Great, Tanqua and Little Karoo; Cape Fold Belt; southwestern and eastern Cape in rante.

4 **Gnidia meyeri**   **

Shrub up to 50 cm. Many thin stems branching from near the ground. Not grazed.

Namaqualand; Great Escarpment; Upper and Great Karoo and Cape Fold Belt on mountain slopes.

5 **Gnidia polycephala**   Januariebos   *

Shrub up to 50 cm. Many thin stems branching from a thick, very short stem. Inflorescence terminal; flowers yellow, tubular. Increases fast in overstocked veld. Not grazed, but poisonous if ingested during flowering stage.

Great Escarpment; Northern, Upper and Great Karoo; southwestern, eastern and northern Cape; Orange Free State; Transvaal; Botswana and Namibia in flats and disturbed areas.

6 **Passerina vulgaris**   bakkersbos   **

Shrub up to 1,2 m. Like the better-known *Passerina filiformis*, early settlers used it to fire ovens when baking bread as it disappeared in a blaze of very hot flame owing to an inflammable secretion from the leaves. Hardly grazed.

Great Escarpment; Upper, Great and Little Karoo; Cape Fold Belt; southwestern, southern and eastern Cape on crowns.

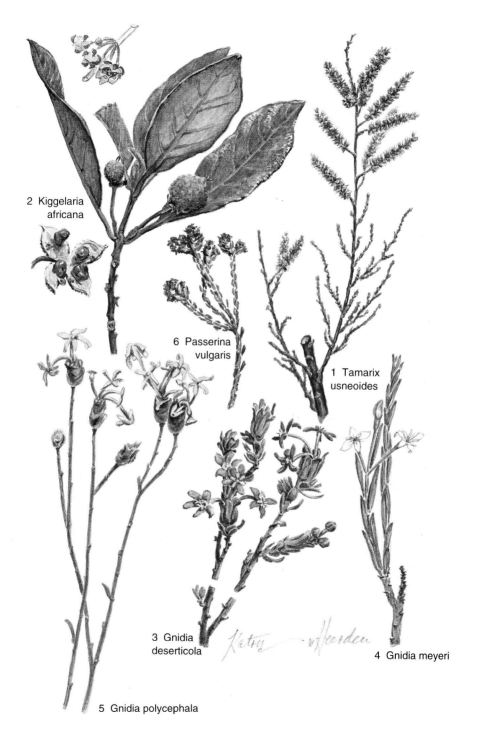

2 Kiggelaria
africana

6 Passerina
vulgaris

1 Tamarix
usneoides

3 Gnidia
deserticola

4 Gnidia meyeri

5 Gnidia polycephala

ARALIACEAE

1 **Cussonia paniculata**   mountain cabbage tree, bergkiepersol   **

Small tree to 5 m. Thick, squat trunk with thick, grey, corky bark. Leaves, which may be deeply serrated, consist of from 7 to 9 leaflets arranged fan-wise. Flowers small and green. Fruit fleshy and purple when mature. Wood of no use, not even for fuel, but roots used by early settlers as coffee substitute. It is starchy, and has also been used by Africans as food. Not grazed.

Great Escarpment; Upper, Great and Little Karoo; Cape Fold Belt; eastern and northern Cape; Orange Free State; Natal; Transvaal; Botswana and Lesotho in kloofs, dry stony hills and mountains.

ONAGRACEAE

2 **Oenothera rosea**   evening primrose, aandblom   **

Erect or sprawling exotic annual herb from South America on a perennial root-stock. Widespread weed in Southern Africa today. Hardly grazed.

Great Escarpment; Upper Karoo; southwestern, eastern and northern Cape; Botswana, Lesotho, Namibia and Swaziland in disturbed areas.

APIACEAE

3 **Deverra denudata** subsp. **aphylla**   wildeseldery, wildevinkel   **

Herb up to 1,2 m. Many green to olive-green, leafless stems emanating from base. Inflorescence, consisting of many small yellow flowers, borne on ends of these stems. When bruised, gives off a characteristic celery smell. Not grazed.

Namaqualand; Great Escarpment; Northern, Upper and Great Karoo; Cape Fold Belt; southwestern, southern, eastern and northern Cape; Transvaal; Botswana and Namibia in seasonal streams, flood plains, flats and crowns.

4 **Heteromorpha arborescens**   parsley tree, kraaihout   **

Tree up to 6 m. Branches straggle with reddish-brown to purplish-brown, smooth, somewhat waxy bark. Light green leaves alternate. Inflorescence a compound umbel with individual flowers small, greenish-white and strong-smelling. Timber quite useless as it is very soft and decays rapidly. Has a wide range of medicinal uses, being used mainly by Blacks who employ an infusion of leaves as an enema, and a decoction for nervous and mental illness. A preparation of leaves for intestinal worms in children is made, and smoke is inhaled for relief of headaches. There are also many other uses, including chewing the fresh root 'to rejuvenate the ageing male'. Not grazed.

Great Escarpment; Upper, Great and Little Karoo; Cape Fold Belt; southwestern, southern, eastern and northern Cape; Orange Free State; Natal; Transvaal; Botswana, Lesotho and Namibia in permanent streams and wet kloofs.

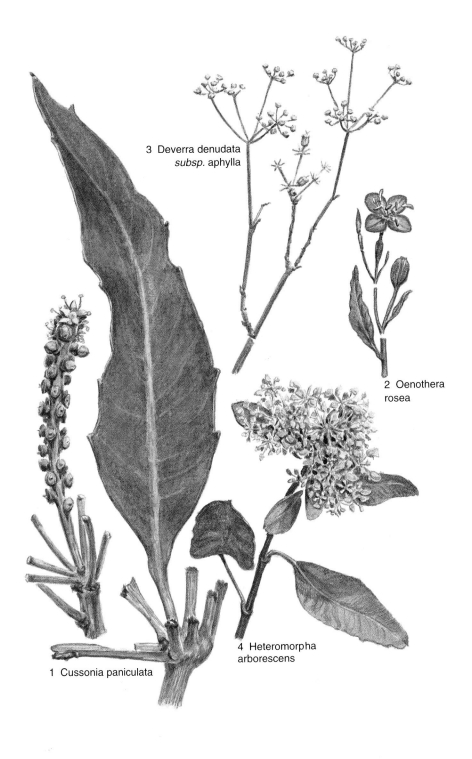

3 Deverra denudata
subsp. aphylla

2 Oenothera
rosea

4 Heteromorpha
arborescens

1 Cussonia paniculata

APIACEAE
1 **Berula erecta** subsp. **thunbergii**   **
Member of carrot family up to 25 cm. Light green, feathery leaves. Inflorescence white to pale yellow. Prefers sandy soil and lots of water. Not grazed.

Great Escarpment; Upper, Great and Little Karoo; Cape Fold Belt; southwestern, southern, eastern and northern Cape; Orange Free State; Natal and Transvaal in permanent streams, flood plains and wet kloofs.

EBENACEAE
2 **Diospyros austro-africana** var. **austro-africana**   kritikom, jakkalsbos   **
Shrub with many branches up to 2,5 m. Bark dark and often found peeling in long strips. Small, alternate leaves ovate and hairy. Flowers creamy-white to pink. Fruit round. Common name, kritikom, derives from original Khoisan who used it to make fire by rubbing the dried sticks together till they flamed. Not grazed.

Namaqualand; Upper Karoo; Great Escarpment; Great and Little Karoo; southwestern, southern, eastern and northern Cape; Orange Free State; Natal; Transvaal and Lesotho in seasonal streams, rante, mountain slopes and kloofs.

3 **Diospyros lycioides**   star apple, bloubos, swartbas   **
Large shrub growing at times to 7 m. Smooth, almost black bark covers stems. Leaves blue-green to green. Fruit round, brown, about 5 to 10 mm in diameter. Flowers small, off-white to yellow, and occur in bunches. There is a superstition that these shrubs attract lightning and that it is dangerous to shelter under one during a thunderstorm. Many older farmers also firmly believe that this shrub grows on a water-bearing vein, while the 'wolwedoring' (*Lycium oxycarpum*) grows on the dolerite dyke. Ripe fruit have been used as a coffee substitute. Hardly grazed, but does supply a certain amount of shelter for the animals.

Throughout southern Africa in permanent and seasonal streams, flood plains, kloofs and wet kloofs.

4 **Euclea crispa**   bush guarri, bosgwarrie   **
Evergreen shrub growing from 1 to 2 m. Bark grey. Variably shaped leaves opposite or alternate. Inconspicuous flowers greenish to yellow or white. Fruit round. A fire fighter's delight as leaves do not come off branches easily, so flames can be beaten out with them. Timber is dark and heavy and was used to make yokes. A decoction made from the black bark from the root is strongly laxative. Fruits edible. Not grazed.

Throughout southern Africa in rante, mountain slopes and kloofs.

4 Euclea crispa

2 Diospyros austro-africana
var. austro-africana

1 Berula erecta
subsp. thunbergii

3 Diospyros lycioides

OLEACEAE
1 **Menodora juncea** blombiesie   ***
Shrub up to 90 cm. Has a broom-like appearance, having many nearly straight, almost leafless branches arising from the base. Flowers large, up to 2,5 cm across, and bright yellow. Fruit a 2-lobed capsule. *Menodora* species have been recorded from southwestern United States of America, Mexico, central and south America and Southern Africa. However, *Menodora juncea* is very distinct from the other two Southern African species and has its allies in the Americas. It may therefore be looked upon as evidence of the surmised land bridge that is thought at one time to have connected South America and Southern Africa. Well grazed.

Namaqualand; Bushmanland; Great Escarpment; Upper, Great and Little Karoo in seasonal streams, flats, apron veld, rante, mountain slopes and kloofs.

2 **Olea europaea** subsp. **africana** wild olive, swartolienhout   ****
Medium sized tree up to 10 m. Bark grey to brown, becoming rough with age. Leaves oblong, glossy dark green to grey-green above, but yellowish often with a covering of silvery or golden-brown scales below. Very small, but strongly scented, white or cream flowers. Ovoid fruit becomes dark brown or black when mature. Timber hard, fine-grained and very durable, works well, takes a fine finish and is very suitable for high-class furniture. Most stands of big trees have been felled for fencing posts. Drought and frost resistant, but very slow growing. Used medicinally for colic, eye lotion and as a gargle. Walking sticks of this wood are still popular among shepherds who, when confronted by thunder weather out in the veld, quickly smoke scrapings from their sticks. This, they believe, prevents their being struck by lightning. Very well grazed, and pastures of these trees kept grazed down to knee height have been advocated.

Throughout southern Africa in permanent and seasonal streams, rante, mountain slopes and kloofs.

LOGANIACEAE
3 **Buddleia glomerata** niesbos, kakkerlak   **
Shrub up to 4 m. Young green branches covered in fine silvery-white hairs, as are undersides of the bluish-green leaves. Yellow inflorescences that appear from spring to autumn form almost spherical heads. Pollen can cause attacks of hay fever. Not grazed.

Great Escarpment; Northern, Upper and Great Karoo; Cape Fold Belt; southwestern, southern, eastern and northern Cape and Orange Free State on mountain slopes and kloofs.

4 **Buddleia salviifolia** mountain sage, bergsalie   **
Shrub up to 4 m. Many long, slender stems with reddish-brown bark. Hairs cover branchlets. Leaves dark green above and rusty or white below. Flowers can vary through white, cream, lilac and purple, and appear in large terminal heads. Strikes easily from cuttings, but as a garden subject, is very prone to attack by insects. Timber hard and heavy, and was used for making assegai shafts and fishing rods. Not grazed.

Great Escarpment; Upper, Great and Little Karoo; Cape Fold Belt; southwestern, southern and eastern Cape; Orange Free State; Natal; Transvaal; Lesotho, Mozambique, Swaziland and Zimbabwe in seasonal streams and kloofs.

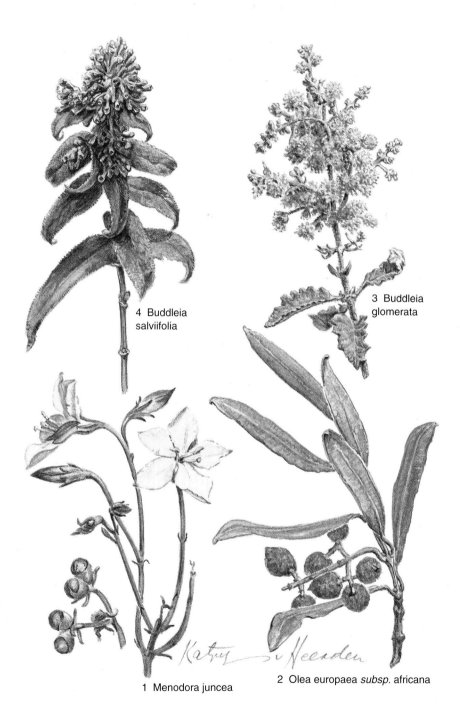

4 Buddleia salviifolia

3 Buddleia glomerata

1 Menodora juncea

2 Olea europaea *subsp*. africana

OLEACEAE
1 **Menodora juncea**   blombiesie   ***
(See page 112)

GENTIANACEAE
2 **Sebaea pentandra**   **
Erect, annual herb up to 25 cm. Can have several stems, densely packed with oval leaves. Many individual flowers on an inflorescence, deep yellow. Not grazed to any extent.

Great Escarpment; Upper Karoo; southwestern Cape and Orange Free State in permanent streams.

APOCYNACEAE
3 **Carissa haematocarpa**   num-num, noem-noem   **
A dark green, evergreen shrub up to 3 m, it is dotted throughout the mountains of the Central Karoo. Oval-shaped leaves are opposite. Distinctive, forked spines cover plant. Masses of strongly scented, cream flowers. The only *Carissa* species to have purple fruit. Birds and children very fond of fruit, and bees make a good honey from the nectar. Very drought resistant. Grazed to a limited extent by animals, particularly goats.

Namaqualand; Great Escarpment; Great and Little Karoo; Cape Fold Belt; southwestern, southern and eastern Cape and Namibia in apron veld, rante, mountain slopes and kloofs.

ASCLEPIADACEAE
4 **Microloma armatum**   ystervarkbossie   ***
[=Microloma massonii]
Shrub up to 50 cm. Fairly straight, green branches end in spines. Flattened, opposite leaves somewhat hairy. Flowers dull yellow and appear along the branches. Seed in a pod that can be up to 5 cm long. Very drought resistant, it responds well to reasonable rains. Not common anywhere, but well grazed where found.

Namaqualand; Bushmanland; Great Escarpment; Northern, Upper and Great Karoo and Namibia in rante.

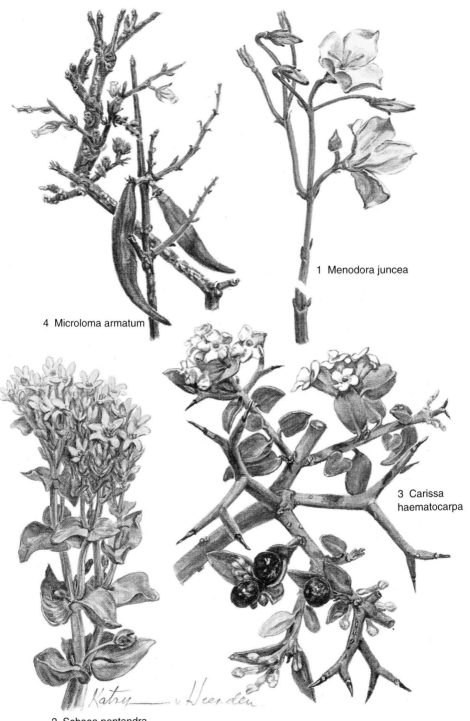

1 Menodora juncea

4 Microloma armatum

3 Carissa haematocarpa

2 Sebaea pentandra

APOCYNACEAE
1 Pachypodium succulentum   dikvoet   **
Succulent dwarf shrub up to 30 cm. Has a very large underground stem. Spines
cover ariel stems. Flowers vary from white, through shades of pink to crimson,
usually with a darker stripe. Tuber is edible, and formed an important part of the
diet of the San. Not grazed.

Great Escarpment; Northern, Upper, Great and Little Karoo; southern, eastern
and northern Cape; Orange Free State and Transvaal in rante and mountain slopes.

ASCLEPIADACEAE
2 Asclepias buchenaviana   mountain milk bush, lammerlat   **
Erect shrub comprising many thin, long (2,5 m), straight, green-blue stems that
exude a milky latex when broken. Leaves very narrow, and may be up to 10 cm
long. Bunches of insignificant yellow-green flowers appear on stems. Seedpods
burst open to liberate the dark brown seed, each attached to its own feathery para-
chute. Very drought resistant, but does not grow in great numbers anywhere. Not
grazed by domestic livestock, though Elegant Grasshoppers are attracted to it, and
swarm into them in their thousands.

Namaqualand; Bushmanland; Great Escarpment; Upper, Great, and Little Karoo;
Orange Free State; Natal and Namibia in seasonal streams, flats and disturbed
areas.

3 Asclepias fruticosa   milkweed, wild cotton, tontelbos   * or **
Erect shrub up to 1,5 m or more. Has many straight stems. Leaves long, narrow
and opposite. Seed contained in a pod. Each seed is attached to a tuft of long,
white, silky hairs that were used when dry, for tinder, as were strands of fibre from
dried branches. These hairs are not unlike commercial cotton, and were used by
Boers in the Anglo-Boer War for makeshift cotton. Latex formed a part of the
arrow-poison made by San hunters. Not normally grazed, except by springbuck.
An excess is toxic as it contains a heart glycoside.

Throughout southern Africa in permanent and seasonal streams, flood plains
and disturbed areas.

4 Sarcostemma viminale   spantou, melktou   *
Sturdy, succulent, leafless creeper that often scrambles over other shrubs and trees.
Grey-green branches jointed and about the thickness of a pencil. When damaged
they exude a sticky, white latex. Not normally grazed, but is toxic to animals when
ingested.

Throughout southern Africa in a wide range of habitats, usually among trees and
bushes.

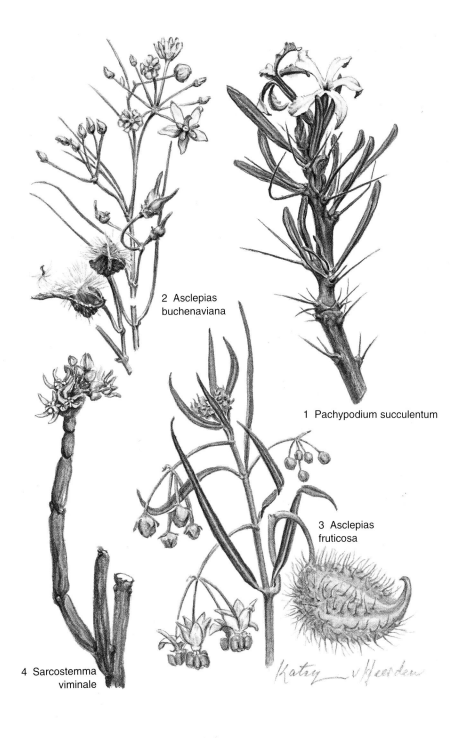

2 Asclepias
buchenaviana

1 Pachypodium succulentum

3 Asclepias
fruticosa

4 Sarcostemma
viminale

Katy — v/Heerden

ASCLEPIADACEAE

1 **Hoodia bainii**   jakkalsghaap, bitterghaap   **

Stem succulent up to 25 cm. A single plant may have many stems, each having 12-15 angles and covered in spines. Earth-coloured flowers with their foetid smell are up to 75 mm in diameter. They appear near the top of the stem and have 5 awn-like points on the rim of the flower. Unlike other family members, this *Hoodia* is inedible, and the early Khoisan people said it was useless even for medicine. Not grazed.

Namaqualand; Bushmanland; Great Escarpment; Northern, Upper, Great and Tanqua Karoo; northern Cape and Namibia in flats and rante.

2 **Pachycymbium miscellum**   **

Inconspicuous, rare asclepiad usually found growing under small shrubs. They do not contribute anything to grazing, but their presence is an indicator of good veld conditions.

Upper and Great Karoo in flats.

3 **Trichocaulon flavum**   soetghaap   **

Like *Pachycymbium miscellum*, this small 'ghaap' does not contribute to the grazing. However, its presence does suggest the availability of seeding and germination habitats.

Great Escarpment; Upper and Great Karoo and Namibia in rante.

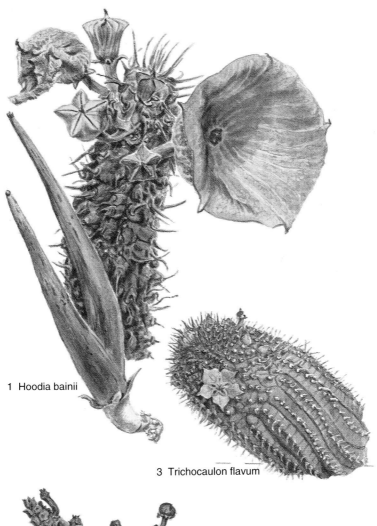

1 Hoodia bainii

3 Trichocaulon flavum

2 Pachycymbium miscellum

Katy — v Heerden

ASCLEPIADACEAE

1 **Duvalia caespitosa** Hotnotstoontjie   **

Small succulent often found hiding beneath other bushes. Sections of stem are rounded and break off easily. Brown flowers have five, long, narrow petals. Not grazed.

Great Escarpment under bushes on apron veld and rante.

2 **Stapelia grandiflora** makghaap, slangghaap   **

[=*Stapelia flavirostris*]

Succulent with 'fingers' reaching 25 cm. Flowers on stalks, are about 50 to 75 mm in diameter and have a strong foetid smell which attracts flies and other insects that then pollinate them. Seed in horns is dispersed by wind when ripe. Only slightly grazed.

Great Escarpment; Northern, Upper, Great and Little Karoo; Cape Fold Belt; southwestern, southern, eastern and northern Cape; Orange Free State; Natal and Transvaal in apron veld and rante.

3 **Stapelia olivacea** agurkie   **

Small succulent whose 'fingers' reach 15 cm. These fingers are stems - each of which flowers only in its early stages. Flowers are about 2,5 cm across, reddish-purple and covered by minute hairs. The 'horns' that appear during summer contain seed. These, if they are not eaten by humans or animals, burst open when ripe to scatter the winged seed. Not grazed.

Great Escarpment; Upper and Great Karoo and northern Cape in apron veld and rante.

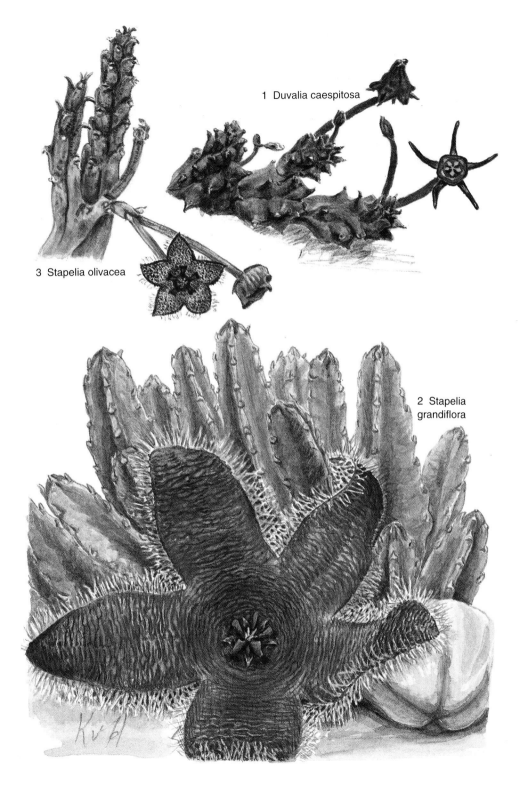

1 Duvalia caespitosa

3 Stapelia olivacea

2 Stapelia grandiflora

CONVOLVULACEAE

1 Convolvulus arvensis   field bindweed, akkerwinde   *

Prostrate or climbing perennial, exotic herb that originated in Europe and Asia, now cosmopolitan. Roots up to 3 m long with a circumference up to 6 m and in deep soils extend to a depth of 9 m. Leaves alternate, arrow-shaped. Seed grey to black, three-angled with a rough texture. New crowns form from buds out of rhizome. Has the capacity of growing in an atmosphere of nitrogen containing some carbonic anhydride and changing it so that it eventually contains more oxygen than free air. Grazed only in conjunction with feed such as grass or lucerne. Great Escarpment; Upper, Great and Little Karoo; southwestern and eastern Cape; Orange Free State; Transvaal and Lesotho in disturbed areas.

2 Convolvulus sagittatus   wild bindweed, bobbejaantou   **

Prostrate or climbing perennial herb with stems up to 3 m. Strong woody taproot. Leaves alternate, variable in shape and size. Has become a serious problem in gardens and lands. Very difficult to eradicate. Hardly grazed. Widespread in sub-Saharan Africa in disturbed areas.

3 Cuscuta campestris   dodder   *

Yellow twining, leafless, parasitic, exotic herb originating in North America. Contains no chlorophyll. Sticks to its host by means of minute suckers that penetrate host's conducting tissue. Now a world wide noxious weed. Often found growing on lucerne. Only means of eradication is to remove infected plants and burn them. Not grazed. Great Escarpment; Upper, Great and Little Karoo; southwestern, southern and eastern Cape; Orange Free State; Natal; Transvaal; Botswana and Lesotho in disturbed areas.

BORAGINACEAE

4 Anchusa capensis   forget-me-not, koringblom   ***

Annual herb up to 60 cm. Stems rough, deeply grooved, hairy. Leaves alternate, hairy on both sides. Inflorescence a panicle with individual blue, tubular flowers. A riparian species often growing in clumps. Reasonably grazed. Throughout the Cape except Bushmanland and Tanqua Karoo; Orange Free State; Transvaal; Lesotho and Namibia in seasonal streams, sandy flats and disturbed areas.

5 Ehretia rigida   Cape lilac, deurmekaarbos   *****

Tree up to 4 m. Drooping branches have smooth greyish bark. Sweetly scented flowers resemble those of true lilac. Fruits edible, bright orange-red when mature. Wood hard, tough, used for making assegai handles and mortars for grinding mealies. Used medicinally and extensively for witchcraft. Very well grazed.

Throughout southern Africa in apron veld, rante, mountain slopes and kloofs.

6 Lobostemon argenteus   agtdaegeneesbos   **

Shrub up to 90 cm with at times a spread of even more. Leaves and stems covered with very fine thorns or stiff hairs. Inflorescence single on a stem with one deep blue flower in the axil of each bract. There are two other agtdaegeneesbosse in the Karoo. The single inflorescence on a stem of *Lobostemon stachydeus* has two blue (shading to pink at the base) flowers in the axils of the bracts, while *Lobostemon fruticosa* has a number of inflorescences on a stem with blue, pink or rarely white flowers. Has been used medicinally, and has the reputation of healing almost any disease within eight days! Not grazed. Namaqualand; Great Escarpment; Great Karoo; Cape Fold Belt; southwestern and southern Cape in moist habitats like seasonal streams and kloofs.

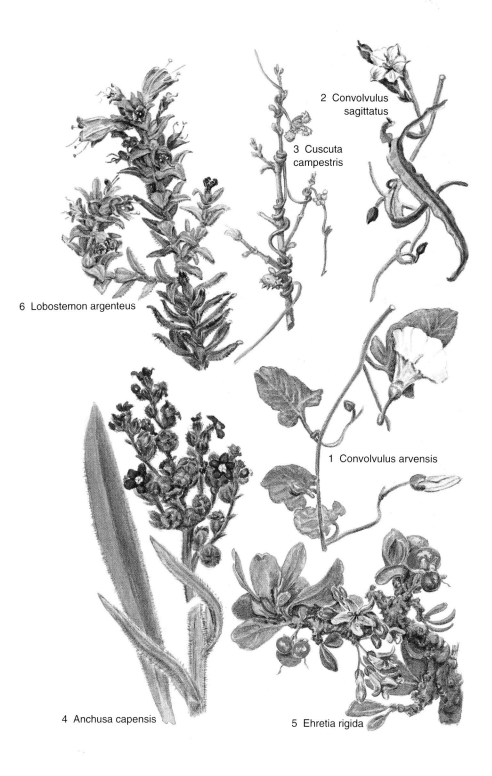

2 Convolvulus
sagittatus

3 Cuscuta
campestris

6 Lobostemon argenteus

1 Convolvulus arvensis

4 Anchusa capensis

5 Ehretia rigida

VERBENACEAE

1 **Lantana rugosa** bird's brandy, wildesalie   **

Erect dwarf shrub up to 1,5 m. Younger branches very hairy, and these and the leaves give off a verbena-like odour when crushed. Fruit purple, edible and fairly extensively used in times of famine. They reportedly stupefy cage birds when over-ripe. Widely used medicinally for conditions ranging from sore eyes to ovarian troubles. Hardly grazed.

Great Escarpment; Northern, Upper, Great and Little Karoo; southern, eastern and northern Cape; Orange Free State; Natal; Transvaal; Botswana, Lesotho, Namibia and Swaziland on crowns.

2 **Plexipus pumilus**   **

Shrub up to 30 cm high and almost twice as wide. Leaves are deeply lobed. Flowers are creamy-white. When crushed the plant has a pleasant smell. Not well grazed.

Namaqualand; Bushmanland; Great Escarpment; Northern and Great Karoo; northern Cape and Botswana in rante and mountain slopes.

LAMIACEAE

3 **Leonotis ocymifolia**   minaret flower, rooidagga, wildedagga   **

Many-stemmed herb up to 150 cm. Much resembles the common *Leonotis leonurus* that grows in many gardens. Not a true dagga and possession is not a criminal offence. Marloth stated that 'the fumes from burning a leaf in an ordinary dagga-pipe are so nauseating that few people, even among the Hottentot (sic!) would venture to use it'. Used extensively medicinally. Not grazed.

Great Escarpment; Great Karoo; southwestern, southern and eastern Cape; Orange Free State; Natal; Transvaal; Lesotho, Namibia and Swaziland in rante, mountain slopes and kloofs.

4 **Mentha longifolia**   wild mint, balderja, ballerja   **

Perennial herb up to 1,5 m. Stems are 4-angled. Leaves opposite. Inflorescence a whorl of mauve, lilac or whitish flowers. Original Nama name meant 'something growing near water'. Used by the Khoisan since early times as a tea and diaphoretic. Bunches were also used to keep flies away. Not grazed.

Widespread throughout Africa and Europe in permanent streams and other wet places.

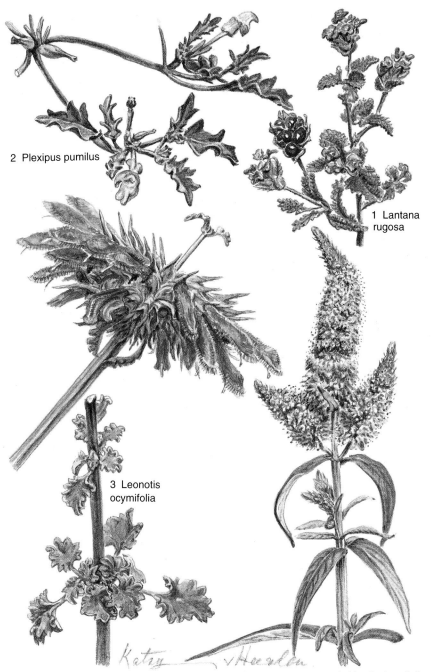

2 Plexipus pumilus

1 Lantana
rugosa

3 Leonotis
ocymifolia

4 Mentha longifolia

LAMIACEAE

1 **Ballota africana**   kattekruie   **

Aromatic herb up to 80 cm. Large round leaves are opposite. Flowers are in dense clusters. All parts are hairy. Very widely used medicinally, particularly for pulmonary complaints and asthmatic conditions. The Khoi used a tea for fevers. Not grazed.

Namaqualand; Great Escarpment; Upper, Great, Tanqua and Little Karoo; Cape Fold Belt; southwestern, southern and eastern Cape; Orange Free State and Namibia in permanent streams and disturbed areas.

2 **Lamium amplexicaule**   turksenael   **

Small annual exotic weed from Europe and Asia, up to 30 cm. Lobed leaves are whorled near tips of otherwise leafless stems, also at base. Flowers also in whorls. A great nuisance in the garden where they appear in their thousands. Can be well grazed, though not always.

Great Escarpment; Great Karoo; eastern Cape and Lesotho in disturbed areas.

3 **Salvia disermas**   grootblousalie, teesalie   **

Aromatic herb up to 1 m. Many branches arise from the rootstock. Leaves are rough with distinct veining. Inflorescence is on the ends of leafless stalks with the flowers in whorls. Used as a tea substitute, and an infusion has been used as a lotion for sores. Only slightly grazed.

Namaqualand; Great Escarpment; Northern, Upper, Great and Little Karoo; Cape Fold Belt; southwestern, southern and northern Cape; Orange Free State; Natal and Transvaal in permanent and seasonal streams and kloofs.

4 **Stachys aurea**   geelteebossie   ****

Much-branched greyish coloured shrub up to 2 m. Leaves have a strong scent. Flowers yellow. Infusions have been used to treat flu and colds. Well grazed.

Namaqualand; Great Escarpment; Little Karoo; southwestern Cape in permanent and seasonal streams and kloofs.

5 **Stachys cuneata**   vaaltee, bergtee   **

Herb to 30 cm. Stems, which vary in colour from grey to off-white, are thin. Leaves are a light blue-green with serrated edges, which, when crushed, give off an unpleasant odour. Flowers are a deep rose colour. Forms dense stands, particularly on mountain slopes. These help to combat soil erosion by holding back sediment in rainwater. Tea can be made from the leaves and stems of the plant. Not grazed by domestic animals, but dassies do appear to take it to some extent.

Namaqualand; Great Escarpment; Northern, Upper and Great Karoo and eastern Cape in seasonal streams, rante, mountain slopes and kloofs.

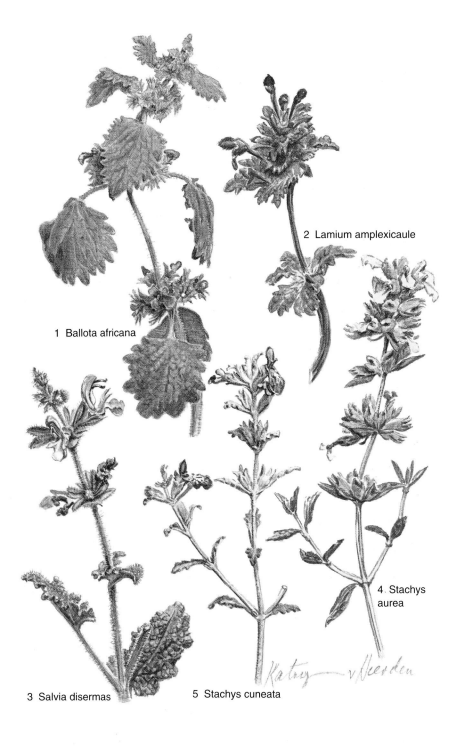

2 Lamium amplexicaule

1 Ballota africana

4. Stachys aurea

3 Salvia disermas

5 Stachys cuneata

SOLANACEAE

1 **Lycium cinereum** kriedoring, slangbessie, kareebos **

Densely branched shrub up to 1 m. Branches end in hard, sharp thorns. Fruit are round, red and edible. Leaves may be either tufted or scattered and are often slightly succulent. Roots spreading from the mother plant at a depth of 20-30 cm cause suckers. They have been used for making almost impenetrable hedges. Not grazed as a rule, though new growth may be taken very well by goats in particular.

Namaqualand; Bushmanland; Great Escarpment; Northern, Upper, Great and Little Karoo; southern, eastern and northern Cape; Orange Free State; Natal and Namibia in seasonal streams, flood plains, flats, apron veld and rante.

2 **Lycium hirsutum** rivierkareedoring, wolwedoring **

Large shrub reaching 3 m. Leaves and young stems are covered with hairs, being the only member of this genus in Southern Africa that has hairy parts. Hairs have a foetid smell. Tubular flowers are creamy white. Only new growth is grazed.

Namaqualand; Great Escarpment; Northern, Upper, Great and Little Karoo; northern Cape; Orange Free State and Namibia in permanent and seasonal streams.

3 **Lycium oxycarpum** wolwedoring **

[=Lycium austrinum]

Large shrub up to 4 m. Has many brittle branches armed with spines. Leaves appear after rains, but they are shed when conditions start to get dry. Lilac to mauve flowers are tubular. Fruit small, red. See *Diospyros lycioides* for an old superstition. Another superstition says that when the leaves fall off the plant a drought is round the corner. Not grazed to any extent, though the shed leaves are sometimes eaten.

Throughout the Cape in permanent and seasonal streams, rante, kloofs and disturbed areas.

4 **Lycium prunus-spinosa** bloukareedoring **

Shrub to 1,25 m much resembling *Lycium cinereum*. Stems are a shiny purple-blue. Bright-red fruit are edible and have been used as a coffee substitute when dried. Only new growth is grazed.

Bushmanland; Great Escarpment; Upper, Great and Little Karoo; southern, eastern and northern Cape; Orange Free State and Namibia in flood plains, flats and disturbed areas.

5 **Nicotiana glauca** wild tobacco, Jantwak, wildetabak *

Small tree up to 5 m. Young branches are green, and all are brittle. Almost invariably some will be dead. Leaves are shiny, large and bunched towards tips of younger branches. Flowers are tubular, yellow and found in bunches. Seed is minute, dark brown, and, because it falls out so soon, very seldom noticed. Introduced to Southern Africa from the Argentine by Baron von Ludwig about 1845 `to supply this treeless country with an ornamental tree'. Has since become very widespread. Short-lived and not very drought resistant, but germinates well in good conditions. Not grazed, and is poisonous to animals and especially ostriches.

Widespread throughout southern Africa in permanent and seasonal streams, flood plains, flats and disturbed areas.

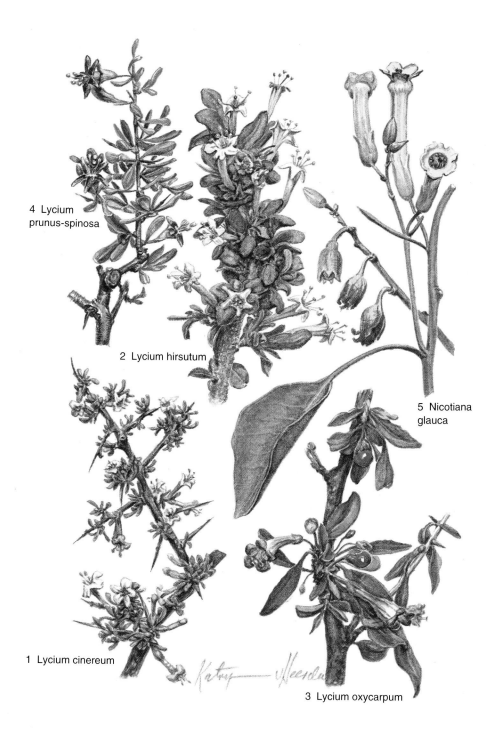

4 Lycium
prunus-spinosa

2 Lycium hirsutum

5 Nicotiana
glauca

1 Lycium cinereum

3 Lycium oxycarpum

SOLANACEAE

1 **Datura stramonium**   stramonium, stinkblaar, olieboom   *
Robust annual up to 1,5 m, probably a native of tropical America, but now cosmopolitan. Stems green or purple. Alternate leaves have coarsely serrated margins. Roughly tubular flowers may be white to purple. Thorny pod contains the seed. Poisonous, one of the earliest poisons known to the old Romans. Widely used for medicinal purposes. Dried leaves smoked for asthma, warmed leaves used as a sedative, and small plugs rolled from leaves used for earache. Not grazed.

Bushmanland; Great Escarpment; Upper and Great Karoo; southwestern, southern, eastern and northern Cape; Orange Free State; Natal; Transvaal; Botswana, Lesotho, Namibia and Swaziland in permanent and seasonal streams and disturbed areas.

2 **Solanum elaeagnifolium**   silverleaf bitter apple, satansbos   *
Newly introduced exotic originating from the USA. Earliest record in the National Herbarium dated 1952. Has become very troublesome on lands since its introduction owing to spreading root system. Ploughing spreads roots and increases the problem. A declared weed. Not grazed.

Great Karoo; southwestern, southern and eastern Cape; Orange Free State and Transvaal on irrigated lands, flood plains, flats and disturbed areas.

3 **Solanum rigescens**   wildelemoentjie   **
Much branched annual or biennial up to 45 cm. Stems covered in spines. Flowers blue. Fruit bright orange-red when ripe. Fumes of heated fruits have been used to relieve toothache. Not grazed.

Great Escarpment; Upper and Great Karoo; eastern, southwestern and southern Cape in seasonal streams, rante, kloofs and disturbed areas.

4 & 5 **Solanum tomentosum** complex   slangappel   **
A variable shrub up to 60 cm. Some may be very spiny, recurved or straight (no. 4), others without (no. 5 and page 132 no. 2). Leaves varying from whitish-green to yellow-green and very hairy. Flowers lilac (no. 4 & 5) or white (page 132 no. 2). Fruit, when ripe, bright orange to red. Not grazed.

Widespread throughout southern Africa in seasonal streams, rante, kloofs and disturbed areas.

130

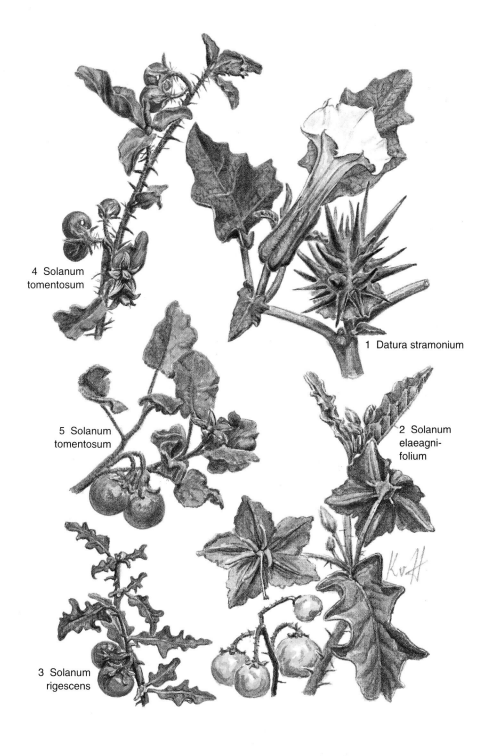

4 Solanum
tomentosum

1 Datura stramonium

5 Solanum
tomentosum

2 Solanum
elaeagni-
folium

3 Solanum
rigescens

SOLANACEAE

1 **Solanum nigrum**   black nightshade, nastergal   **

Native of Europe up to 1 m. Erect, branched annual or biennial. Green to brownish stems often groved, slightly pubescent or sometimes glabrescent. Alternate leaves lanceolate to ovate. Fruit black when ripe. Europeans regard fruit as poisonous, but here only unripe fruit is poisonous. Ripe fruit is used for making jam. Can produce vomiting if too many fruits eaten. Used medicinally for treating convulsions, abdominal upsets, ringworm and malaria. Also used to disinfect anthrax-infested meat and treat anthrax pustules. Not grazed.

Widespread throughout southern Africa in seasonal streams, kloofs and disturbed areas.

2 **Solanum tomentosum** complex   slangappel   **

See page 130.

3 **Withania somnifera**   winter cherry, geneesbossie, wilde-appelliefie   **

Branched perennial up to 80 cm. Often wider than high. Leaves alternate. Flowers inconspicuous. Fruits bright red in membranous pods resemble gooseberries. Can become a weed in tramped out veld, dongas and on roadsides. Used medicinally for treating colds and chills, ringworm, syphilitic sores, erysipelas and many other conditions. Also used as an insecticide. Not grazed.

Great Escarpment; Upper, Great and Little Karoo; southern, eastern and northern Cape; Orange Free State; Transvaal; Botswana, Lesotho, Mozambique, Namibia, Swaziland and Zimbabwe in permanent and seasonal streams, kloofs and disturbed areas.

SCROPHULARIACEAE

4 **Limosella grandiflora**   slangkos   **

[=*Limosella capensis*]

Small water-loving herb. Leaves spade-shaped. Flowers blue-white. Roots from branches, so long strings of plants may all be connected. Not grazed.

Namaqualand; Great Escarpment; Northern, Upper and Great Karoo; Cape Fold Belt; southwestern, southern, eastern and northern Cape; Orange Free State; Lesotho and Namibia in permanent streams and other waterlogged areas.

5 **Nemesia fruticans**   leeubekkie, maagpynblommetjie   **

Annual or biennial up to 60 cm, though usually smaller. Flowers variable, but always resemble those of a snap-dragon. Hardly grazed.

Great Escarpment; Northern, Upper, Great, Tanqua and Little Karoo; southwestern, southern, eastern and northern Cape; Orange Free State; Natal; Transvaal; Lesotho and Namibia in permanent and seasonal streams and disturbed areas.

6 **Zaluzianskya violacea**   drumsticks   **

Small annual growing from a perennial rootstock to 10 cm. Usually found growing in sandy places. Hardly grazed.

Namaqualand; Bushmanland; Great Escarpment; Great, Tanqua and Little Karoo; Cape Fold Belt; southwestern, southern and northern Cape in seasonal streams and disturbed areas.

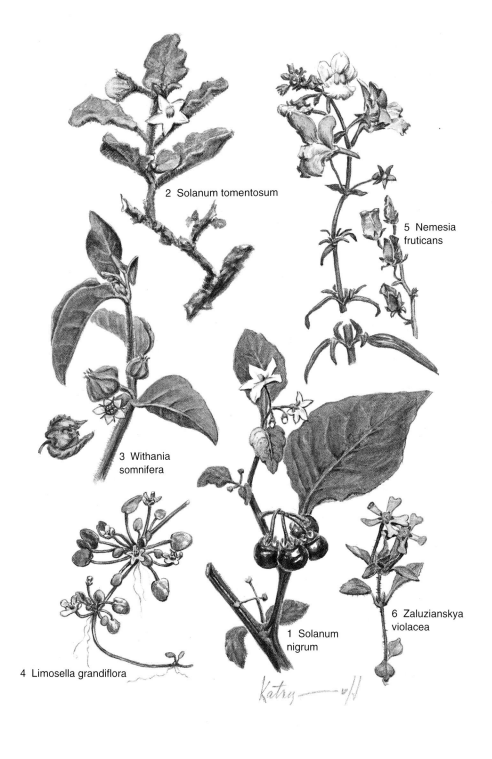

2 Solanum tomentosum

5 Nemesia
fruticans

3 Withania
somnifera

4 Limosella grandiflora

1 Solanum
nigrum

6 Zaluzianskya
violacea

Katry — w/H

SCROPHULARIACEAE

1 Aptosimum indivisum   Karoo violet, Karooviooltjie   **
Strikingly beautiful shrublet up to 7 cm. Long, dark-green, oval leaves reach
15x3 mm. Crown densely packed and seldom exceeds 15 cm diameter. Many deep
blue to purple trumpetlike flowers. Has a long, strong taproot that makes it a difficult subject to transplant. Flowers in spring and summer, though in common with
most Karoo plants, flowers are to be found at almost any time after rains. Grazed
by sheep and goats.
    Namaqualand; Bushmanland; Great Escarpment; Northern, Upper, Great and
Little Karoo; Cape Fold Belt; southwestern and northern Cape; Orange Free State;
Transvaal and Botswana in flood plains, flats, apron veld and rante.

2 Aptosimum procumbens   carpet flower, kankerbos   **
[=Aptosimum depressum]
Forms 'carpets' of up to 1 m diameter. When in full bloom it is covered with lilac,
trumpet-shaped flowers that can appear at any time of the year. Although favour-
ing disturbed or bare ground, it does not indicate condition of the veld. Used medicinally, and also in the treatment of 'krimpsiekte' in sheep. Seed sent to England by
both Burchell and Ecklon was cultivated there as an ornamental. Not much grazed,
though Merino wethers take it during winter.
    Namaqualand; Bushmanland; Great Escarpment; Northern, Upper, Great and
Little Karoo; southern, eastern and northern Cape; Transvaal and Botswana in
flood plains, flats, rante, crowns and disturbed ground.

3 Aptosimum spinescens   doringviooltjie, kankerbossie   **
Distinctive, branched shrublet up to 30 cm. Needle-like, spiny leaves cover stems.
Tubular, blue flowers scattered among leaves. Leaves have been used as a cancer-
cure. Hardly grazed.
    Namaqualand; Bushmanland; Great Escarpment; Northern, Upper, Great and
Little Karoo; northern Cape and Namibia in flood plains, flats and mountain
slopes.

4 Peliostomum leucorrhizum   springbokbos, veld violet   ***
Small, laxly branched shrub up to 25 cm. Narrow, alternate leaves. Deep blue flowers appear in axils of leaves. Very well grazed, but there is not much quantity as
they are never very plentiful.
    Namaqualand; Bushmanland; Great Escarpment; Northern, Upper, Great and
Little Karoo; northern Cape; Orange Free State; Transvaal and Namibia in seasonal
streams, flood plains, flats, apron veld and rante.

5 Aptosimum sp.   Karoo violet, Karooviooltjie   ***
Semi-prostate shrub to 15 cm. Pale lilac flower larger than those of other species
described in this book. Well grazed.
    Great Karoo on limestone outcrops in flats.

3 Aptosimum spinescens

4 Peliostomum leucorrhizum

1 Aptosimum indivisum

5 Aptosimum *sp.*

2 Aptosimum procumbens

SCROPHULARIACEAE

1 Jamesbrittenia tysonii   witbergheuning Karoo, witsafraanbos   ****
[=Sutera tysonii]

Shrub to 35 cm. Leaves have pleasant, though strong smell. In a good season it can be seen from a distance as it is covered in white flowers. Very well grazed.

Great Escarpment in seasonal streams, rante, mountain slopes, kloofs, crowns and disturbed areas.

2 Jamesbrittenia atropurpurea   geelblommetjie, bruinsafraanbos   ***
[=Sutera atropurpurea]

Shrub up to 60 cm. Leaves opposite, small and sparse on comparatively long stems. Brown flowers form a cross and are not easily seen. Once used exclusively by Voortrekkers to dye their linen, leather and furniture. Well grazed.

Namaqualand; Bushmanland; Great Escarpment; Upper, Great and Little Karoo; southern, eastern and northern Cape; Orange Free State; Natal; Transvaal; Botswana and Namibia in flats, apron veld, rante and mountain slopes.

3 & 4 Sutera halimifolia   ***

Shrub up to 20 cm. Flowers light purple to lilac or white. Well grazed.

Great Escarpment; Northern, Upper, Great and Little Karoo; eastern and northern Cape and Orange Free State in apron veld, rante, mountain slopes and kloofs.

5 Sutera uncinata   **
[=Sutera linifolia]

Erect shrublet up to 45 cm. Many branches. Flowers mauve. Grazed to a limited degree.

Great Escarpment; Great Karoo; Cape Fold Belt; southwestern and southern Cape and Orange Free State in rante and mountain slopes.

6 Veronica anagallis-aquatica   water speedwell, waterereprys   **

Erect annual herb up to 60 cm. Leaves opposite, lanceolate and clasp stem at base. Fruits hairy and cling to wool, clothing, etc. A troublesome weed in gardens. Hardly grazed.

Widespread in southern Africa in permanent streams and other damp and wet places.

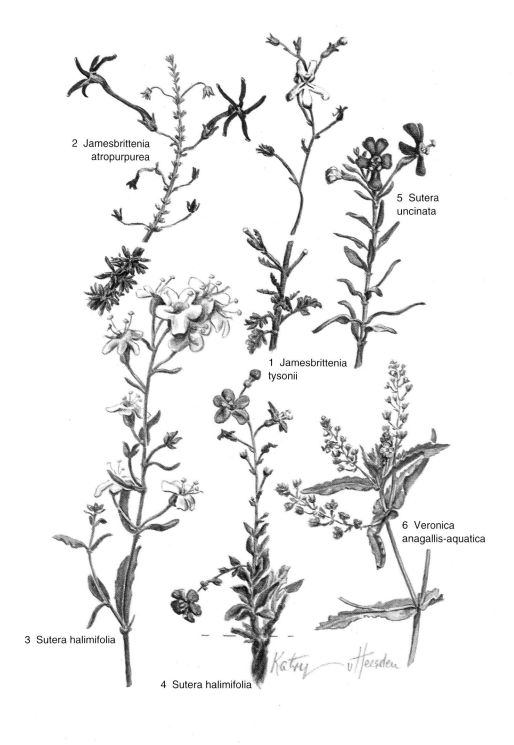

2 Jamesbrittenia atropurpurea

5 Sutera uncinata

1 Jamesbrittenia tysonii

6 Veronica anagallis-aquatica

3 Sutera halimifolia

4 Sutera halimifolia

SCROPHULARIACEAE

1 Diascia capsularis ⁕⁕

Straggly herb reaching 40 cm. Pea-like flowers deep pink. Well grazed, but does not provide very much bulk.

Namaqualand; Great Escarpment; Upper and Great Karoo; southwestern and eastern Cape; Orange Free State; Natal and Lesotho on mountain slopes and crowns.

2 Harveya purpurea ⁕⁕

A small parasite that appears in the open spaces between tufts of grass. It may reach 5 cm. Not grazed.

Great Escarpment on crowns.

SELAGINACEAE

3 Hebenstretia robusta ⁕⁕

Perennial shrub up to 50 cm. Flowers white with an orange marking. Not much grazed.

Namaqualand; Great Escarpment; Upper and Little Karoo; Cape Fold Belt; southwestern and southern Cape in flats, mountain slopes and kloofs.

4 Selago albida witaarbos ⁕⁕⁕

Branched, perennial shrub up to 60 cm. Inflorescence in a terminal panicle and flowers may be white to lilac and even purple. Easily confused with *Walafrida geniculata*, especially when it has purple flowers. Inflorescence is generally rounder in *Selago* and longer in *Walafrida*. Well grazed.

Widespread in southern Africa in a wide range of habitats.

5 Selago speciosa amandelaarbossie ⁕⁕⁕

Shrub up to 70 cm. Leaves alternate, and often have many insect galls. Flowers give off a very strong almond smell towards evening. Grazed.

Great Escarpment; Upper Karoo and eastern Cape on rante, mountain slopes and crowns.

6 Walafrida gracilis honde-kak-en-pisbos ⁕⁕

Shrub up to 35 cm. Flowers white. Has an unpleasant, foetid smell. Hardly grazed.

Great Escarpment and Great Karoo on mountain slopes and crowns.

7 Walafrida geniculata persaarbos ⁕⁕⁕⁕

Shrub up to 40 cm. Found in two forms – female only and bisexual. In the latter inflorescences are fuller and rounder than in female only form. Flowers variable, ranging from white through pink to purple. May easily be confused with *Selago albida* (witaarbos). Very drought-resistant. Very well grazed by all livestock.

Namaqualand; Great Escarpment; Upper, Great and Little Karoo; Cape Fold Belt; southern, eastern and northern Cape and Orange Free State in flats, apron veld, rante and mountain slopes.

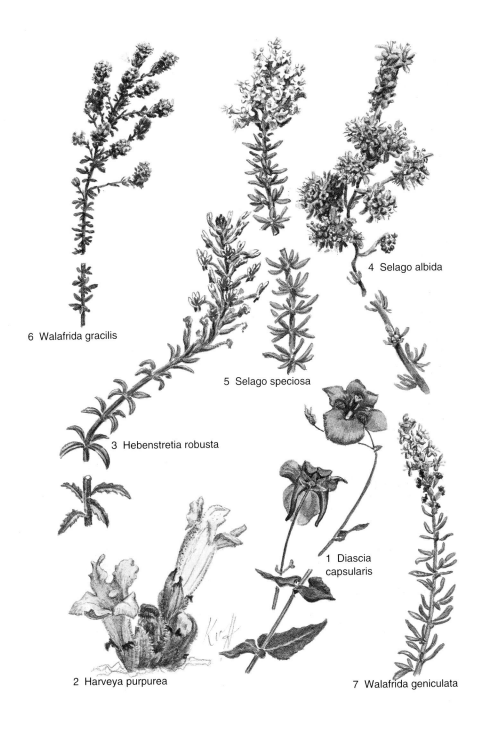

6 Walafrida gracilis

4 Selago albida

5 Selago speciosa

3 Hebenstretia robusta

1 Diascia capsularis

2 Harveya purpurea

7 Walafrida geniculata

BIGNONIACEAE

1 **Rhigozum obovatum**   wild pomegranate, Karoo gold, geelgranaat   *****
Tall, woody shrub up to 2 m. Hard, spiny branches growing in all directions, make
it a formidable-looking plant. Leaves are small, roundish and fall off in dry periods. Yellow flowers cover the shrub in good seasons, making it one of the Karoo's
most spectacular plants. It can start blooming within only a few days of good rains.
However, not all plants in a given community flower simultaneously. Pods remain
on the plant after releasing seed, making a very characteristic rattle in the wind.
Very drought resistant. Very palatable to smallstock. Has been known to be grazed
down to only a few centimeters.
   Great Escarpment; Upper, Great and Little Karoo; southern, eastern and northern
Cape; Orange Free State; Transvaal and Namibia in flood plains, flats, apron veld,
rante and mountain slopes.

2 **Rhigozum trichotomum**   driedoring   * or **
Shrub up to 1 m. Flowers about 4 cm in diameter and vary from white to pale yel-
low or even pale red. Regarded as invasive as it now covers thousands of ha in the
Karoo. Hardly grazed.
   Bushmanland; Great Escarpment; Northern and Great Karoo; eastern and north-
ern Cape; Orange Free State; Botswana and Namibia in flood plains and flats.

3 **Sesamum capense**   Aprilbaadjie   **
Annual up to, at times, 60 cm. Leaves opposite. Flowers solitary, deep pink and
very slightly hairy. Usually grow in early summer, and not April as the common
name suggests. Not grazed.
   Namaqualand; Bushmanland; Great Escarpment; Northern, Upper and Great
Karoo; southwestern and northern Cape; Orange Free State; Transvaal and
Namibia in flats and disturbed areas.

ACANTHACEAE

4 **Barleria stimulans**   skerpioenbos   **
Shrub up to 50 cm. Very spiny. Flowers off-white and about 30 mm in diameter.
Not grazed.
   Great Escarpment; Great Karoo; southwestern and southern Cape in apron veld,
rante, mountain slopes, kloofs and crowns.

4 Barleria stimulans

3 Sesamum capense

1 Rhigozum obovatum

2 Rhigozum trichotomum

ACANTHACEAE

1 **Acanthopsis disperma**   verneukhalfmensie   **

Thorny, low-growing shrub seldom more than 15 cm high. Has sausage-like stems. Leaves are small, and, like stems, carry many sharp spines. Tubular, blue flowers. Not drought-resistant, but seed germinates readily. Many young plants reach maturity. Not grazed.

Namaqualand; Bushmanland; Great Escarpment; Northern and Great Karoo; southwestern, southern and northern Cape and Namibia on mountain slopes and crowns.

2 **Blepharis mitrata**   klapperbossie   **

Small, prostrate and very spiny shrub. Flowers blue to white. Not grazed.

Bushmanland; Great Escarpment; Northern, Upper, Great and Little Karoo; northern Cape and Namibia in flood plains, flats, apron veld, rante and disturbed areas in rocky terrain.

3 **Justicia orchioides**   ribbokbos   **

Shrub up to 1,75 m. Many light to dark grey brittle stems. Oval leaves are blue-green. Snapdragon-like flowers off-white. Small pod contains seed. Grazed by animals when found.

Namaqualand; Great Escarpment; Upper and Little Karoo; southwestern, southern, eastern and northern Cape in seasonal streams, flood plains and flats.

4 **Monechma incanum**   skaapbloubossie, netvetbossie   ****

Common shrub up to 80 cm. Branches often curve downwards to anchor. Simple, opposite leaves give a bluish-grey appearance. Palatable, and gives a good amount of feed when grazed.

Great Escarpment; Northern, Upper, Great and Little Karoo; Cape Fold Belt; northern Cape; Orange Free State; Botswana and Namibia in seasonal streams, flats and apron veld usually in sandy soil.

5 **Monechma spartioides**   maklikbreekbos   ***

Shrub up to 50 cm. Few leaves on striking white stems because they tend to fall off as the countryside dries off. Oval leaves are dark green. Flowers, which resemble those of a snap-dragon, are white or sometimes light lilac. Responds well to even light rains, and is one of the first to recover from a drought. Well grazed by small-stock.

Namaqualand; Bushmanland; Great Escarpment; Northern, Upper, Great and Little Karoo; Cape Fold Belt; southwestern, southern and northern Cape; Transvaal and Namibia in seasonal streams and a wide range of habitats.

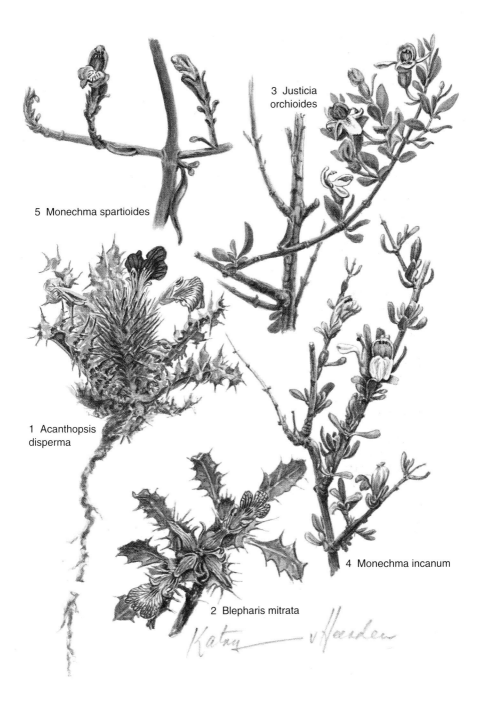

5 Monechma spartioides

3 Justicia orchioides

1 Acanthopsis disperma

4 Monechma incanum

2 Blepharis mitrata

RUBIACEAE

1 **Anthospermum spathulatum** subsp. **spathulatum** jakkalsstert ****
[=Anthospermum aethiopicum]
Shrub up to 25 cm. Often confused with *Nenax microphylla* as it resembles young plants of that species. Flowers on upper part of long false spikes. Usually found in dolerite. Very well grazed.
Great Escarpment; Upper and Great Karoo; southwestern, southern and eastern Cape in apron veld, rante, mountain slopes and kloofs.

2 **Galium tomentosum** old man's beard, rooivergeet, kleefgras **
Clinging creeper that can easily cover an entire tree. Each leaf has a very small recurved spine on its tip which grips fingers and clothes alike. Flowers minute. Seed fairly large, round black fruit. Used medicinally, especially for sore backs. Not grazed.
Namaqualand; Great Escarpment; Upper, Great and Little Karoo; Cape Fold Belt; southwestern, southern and eastern Cape and Namibia in permanent and seasonal streams and kloofs.

3 **Nenax microphylla** daggapit *****
Compact, hardy shrub up to 30 cm. Leaves small, and curve backward on stems. Flowers insignificant. Fruits in a good year are very conspicuous, being round, reddish, about the size of peppercorns. Seed was used as a dagga substitute by the Khoisan. One of the most valuable Karoo plants. Very eagerly grazed by all types of animals.
Great Escarpment; Northern, Upper and Great Karoo; southwestern, eastern and northern Cape and Orange Free State in rante, mountain slopes, kloofs and crowns.

DIPSACACEAE

4 **Scabiosa columbaria** rice flower, koringblom, bitterbos **
Shrub up to 50 cm from a perennial rootstock. Basal leaves in a rosette. A bitter decoction made from leaves is used medicinally. Hardly grazed.
Widespread throughout southern africa in disturbed areas.

PLANTAGINACEAE

5 **Plantago lanceolata** lamb's tongue, ribgras, tongblaar ***
Native of Europe introduced to the Cape at a very early stage and now spread throughout the Republic. Perennial with strong roots up to 60 cm. Strongly ribbed leaves grow in a rosette. Produces large quantities of pollen and is often the cause of severe hay fever. Animals are very partial to it, and once farmers considered planting it.
Widespread in the RSA, Botswana, Lesotho and Namibia in permanent streams and disturbed areas.

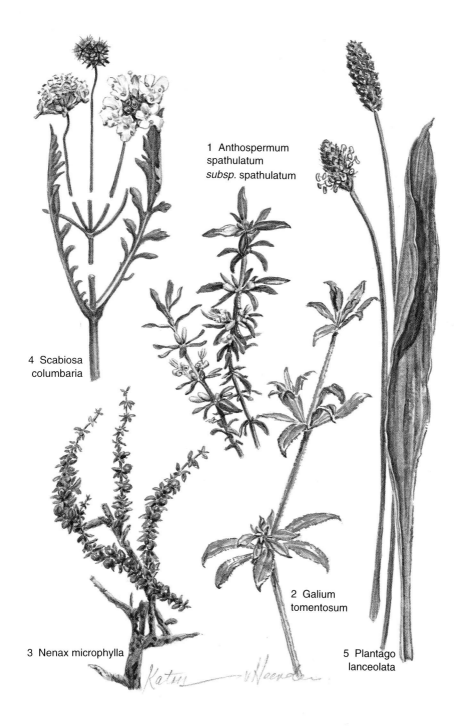

1 Anthospermum
spathulatum
subsp. spathulatum

4 Scabiosa
columbaria

3 Nenax microphylla

2 Galium
tomentosum

5 Plantago
lanceolata

CUCURBITACEAE

1 **Citrullus lanatus**   t'samma melon   **

Creeper with long, trailing branches whose tendrils fasten to any projections. Flowers yellow. Seed contained in a green and yellow melon up to 15 cm in diameter. From early times this melon has been used by man and animals for both food and water. It enabled man to cross the dessert from Botswana to Namibia by oxwagon in good t'samma seasons. Melons were also cooked, and the seed is very sustaining. There appear to be two varieties of this plant. One has a bitter taste and is unfit for human consumption as its cucurbitacin content is too high. An improved variety of the t'samma melon is commonly cultivated. Not noticeably grazed by livestock while more palatable feed is available in the veld.

   Namaqualand; Great Escarpment; Upper, Great and Tanqua Karoo; eastern and northern Cape; Botswana, Lesotho, Mozambique and Namibia in seasonal streams, flood plains, flats and disturbed areas.

2 **Cucumis myriocarpus**   bitterappel   * or **

Much resembles *Cucumis africanus* except that fruit is round and much smaller. Very poisonous and cannot be eaten even when cooked. Not grazed.

   Namaqualand; Bushmanland; Great Escarpment; Northern, Upper and Great Karoo; northern Cape; Transvaal; Botswana and Namibia in seasonal streams, flood plains, flats and disturbed areas.

3 **Cucumis africanus**   wild cucumber, agurkie, doringkomkommer   * or **

Spreading annual on a perennial rootstock. Leaves resemble those of a watermelon. Flowers yellow. Fruit oblong with dark green bands in their length and rows of stiff hairs or soft thorns. When ripe they turn bright yellow. Poisonous when raw, and has caused deaths of both livestock and people. However, when cooked they have been used as pickles. Not grazed.

   Namaqualand; Bushmanland; Great Escarpment; Northern, Upper and Great Karoo; northern Cape; Transvaal; Botswana and Namibia in seasonal streams, flood plains, flats and disturbed areas.

4 **Cucumis zeyheri**   bitterappel   **

Scrambler. Produces medium-sized fruit that turn yellow when ripe. Not grazed.

   Great Escarpment; Upper Karoo; eastern and northern Cape; Orange Free State; Natal; Transvaal; Botswana and Namibia in seasonal streams, flood plains, flats and disturbed areas.

5 **Kedrostis africana**   Cape bryony, basterdawidjieswortel   **

Climber arising from large tuber. Stems have tendrils. Leaves alternate. Flowers greenish-yellow to yellow. Fruit green, turning to bright red when ripe. Infusion in wine and brandy is used as a purgative. Not grazed.

   Namaqualand; Great Escarpment; Great Karoo; northern and eastern Cape; Transvaal; Botswana and Namibia in flats and rante

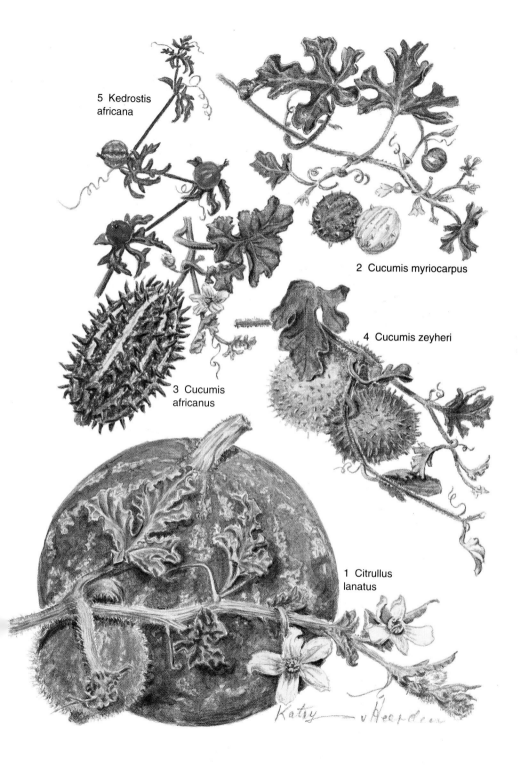

5 Kedrostis
africana

2 Cucumis myriocarpus

4 Cucumis zeyheri

3 Cucumis
africanus

1 Citrullus
lanatus

Katry   v Heerden

CAMPANULACEAE
1 Lightfootia nodosa muistepelkaroo ******

Shrub up to 60 cm. Alternate leaves small and narrow and have a tendency to curl backward. Withstands drought well, but takes a long time to respond to rain. Not a good fodder bush.

Great Escarpment; Northern, Upper, Great and Little Karoo; Cape Fold Belt; southwestern, southern, eastern and northern Cape and Orange Free State in apron veld, rante, mountain slopes, kloofs and crowns.

LOBELIACEAE
2 Lobelia thermalis ******

Low-growing herb making attractive ground cover if not supported. Trailing stems can reach to almost 1 m. Grazed to a limited extent.

Great Escarpment; Northern, Upper and Great Karoo; southern, eastern and northern Cape; Orange Free State; Transvaal; Botswana and Namibia in permanent and seasonal streams.

ASTERACEAE
3 Senecio vimineus ******

Straggly shrub up to 50 cm. Leaves have a few serrations near their base. Flowers yellow. Only slightly grazed. Great Escarpment; Great Karoo; Orange Free State; Transvaal and Lesotho in flats and disturbed areas.

4 Athanasia microcephala ******

Lax shrub up to 1,2 m. Inflorescences terminal with yellow flowers. Not grazed.

Namaqualand; Great Escarpment; Upper and Great Karoo on mountain slopes and disturbed areas.

5 Cineraria lobata ******

Smallish perennial of dry areas. Flowers yellow. Leaves lobed. Hardly grazed.

Namaqualand; Great Escarpment; Upper, Great and Little Karoo; Cape Fold Belt; southwestern, southern and eastern Cape and Lesotho in seasonal streams, rante and mountain slopes.

6 Dicoma capensis karmedik ******

Herb with trailing stems containing a milky latex and growing from a perennial, thickened, woody rootstock. Widely used medicinally for upset stomachs. Slightly grazed. Namaqualand; Bushmanland; Great Escarpment; Northern, Upper and Great Karoo; northern Cape; Botswana and Namibia in seasonal streams, flats, apron veld, rante and disturbed areas.

7 Tagetes minuta Mexican marigold, khakibos ******

Annual, exotic, summer herb, up to 1,2 m. Introduced from South America via United States of America by the British during the Anglo-Boer War. Now spread throughout Republic. Often takes over waste land if left unhindered. Ash mixed with tobacco used as snuff. Anti-flea spray made from the oily sap. Can eradicate eelworm if left to grow where that pest occurs. May be used to advantage as a green manure. Not grazed.

Great Escarpment; Upper and Great Karoo; southwestern, southern, eastern and northern Cape; Orange Free State; Natal; Transvaal; Botswana, Lesotho, Namibia and Swaziland in seasonal streams and disturbed areas.

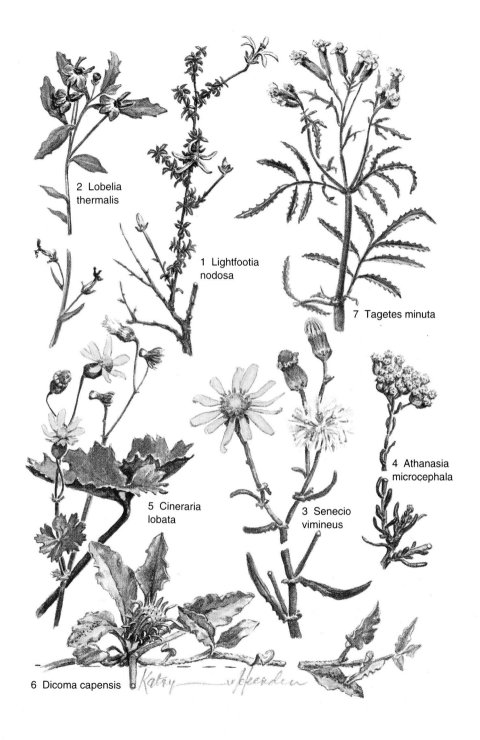

2 Lobelia thermalis

1 Lightfootia nodosa

7 Tagetes minuta

4 Athanasia microcephala

5 Cineraria lobata

3 Senecio vimineus

6 Dicoma capensis

Katry v Heerden

ASTERACEAE

1 **Arctotis leiocarpa**   gousblom   **
Annual up to 40 cm. White ray florets, while the disc florets may sometimes have a
black centre. Germinate particularly well after good spring rains, and may then
cover parts of the countryside. Grazed, but tend to make milk very bitter.
   Namaqualand; Bushmanland; Great Escarpment; Northern, Upper and Great
Karoo; northern Cape and Namibia in flats and disturbed areas.

2 **Arctotis sulcocarpa**   gousblom   **
Small annual with yellow ray and disc florets. Does not grow as profusely as
Arctotis leiocarpa but is possibly more regular. Grazed.
   Great Escarpment; Great and Little Karoo and southwestern Cape in flood plains
and flats.

3 **Athanasia minuta**   vuursiektebossie   *
[=*Asaemia axillaris*]
Shrub up to 50 cm. Yellowish-brown stems end in sharp spines. Sometimes occurs
as an invader, and always grows near water or damp areas. When grazed it causes
secondary photosensitization, particularly of sheep and goats. This is much the
same as 'dikkop' caused by *Tribulus terrestris*.
   Namaqualand; Bushmanland; Upper and Great Karoo; eastern Cape and
Namibia in permanent streams, flood plains, pans and waterlogged disturbed
areas.

4 **Gazania krebsiana**   gazania, botterblom   ***
Small annual up to 15 cm. Often wider than high. Flowers are mainly orange as ray
florets are large with a dark patch at the base. Disc florets are the same colour as
the outer parts of the rays. Strap-shaped leaves are white-woolly below, dark green
above and arise as a rosette. A few leaves are coarsely serrated. Seed germinates
particularly well after good spring rains. Well grazed.
   Widespread in southern Africa in seasonal streams, flood plains, flats, apron
veld, rante and disturbed areas.

5 **Gazania lichtensteinii**   gazania, botterblom   ***
Small annual up to 15 cm. It may be wider than high. Leaves slightly hairy and
may have spines on margins. Disc florets are light yellow and more rounded than
those of *Gazania krebsiana*. Each has a small black dot near the base. Leaves have
toothed margins and are slightly hairy. Grazed.
   Namaqualand; Bushmanland; Great Escarpment; Northern, Upper, Great,
Tanqua and Little Karoo; southwestern and northern Cape; Transvaal and Namibia
in seasonal streams, flats, rante and disturbed areas.

6 **Senecio leptophyllus**   **
Branched shrub up to 60 cm. Yellow flowers. Not much grazed.
   Great Escarpment; Great Karoo; southern and eastern Cape in seasonal streams
and disturbed areas

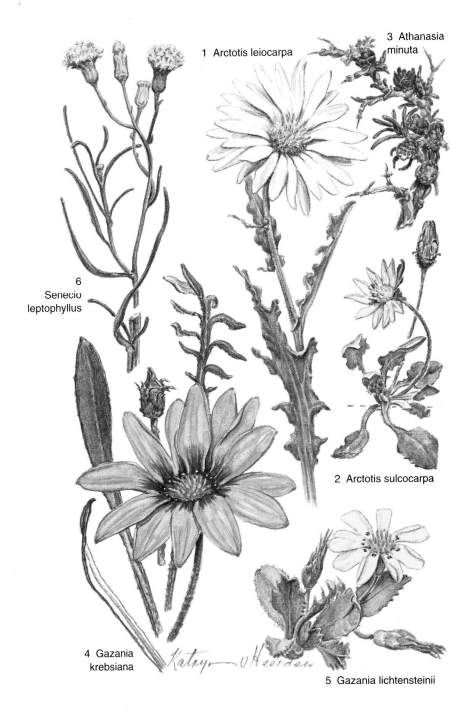

1 Arctotis leiocarpa

3 Athanasia minuta

6 Senecio leptophyllus

2 Arctotis sulcocarpa

4 Gazania krebsiana

5 Gazania lichtensteinii

ASTERACEAE

1 Berkheya glabrata   yellow thistle, geeldissel   **

Annual up to 1,25 m. Covered in spines. Yellow, spiny flowers appear near tops of stems. Not grazed.

Namaqualand; Great Escarpment; Upper and Great Karoo; Cape Fold Belt; southwestern and eastern Cape in permanent and seasonal streams, rante, mountain slopes and disturbed areas.

2 Berkheya spinosa   perdebos   **

Shrub up to 40 cm. Covered in spines - stems, leaves and flowers are all spiny. Leaves have toothed margins. Flowers are yellow. Not grazed.

Great Escarpment; Great and Little Karoo; and southwestern Cape in seasonal streams, flats, apron veld, mountain slopes, rante and crowns.

3 Berkheya heterophylla subsp. **radiata**   graweelwortel   **

Low-growing and spreading shrub covered in spines. Even more spiny than *Berkheya spinosa*. Can cover an area of several square meters with many new plants taking root. Leaves opposite. Flowers yellow. Used medicinally since about 1830 for kidney stones. Not grazed.

Great Escarpment; Little Karoo; eastern, southern and southwestern Cape as well as Cape Fold Belt in mountain slopes and crowns

4 Cirsium vulgare   Canada thistle, Kanadadissel   *

Exotic, a native of Europe and Asia that has spread throughout the world. Erect annual or biennial up to 1 m. Leaves deeply lobed and covered in spines and hairs. Stems very spiny, as are the violet-blue flowers. An extremely troublesome weed that is difficult to eradicate as it has an exceptionally strong root system that may reach up to 90 cm underground. Propagates by suckers from roots of established plants and also from seed. Used medicinally as a brandy tincture to improve appetite, applied to ringworm and used as a diarrhoea remedy. Not grazed.

Great Escarpment; Great Karoo; southwestern, southern and eastern Cape; Orange Free State; Natal; Transvaal and Lesotho in permanent and seasonal streams, flood plains and disturbed areas.

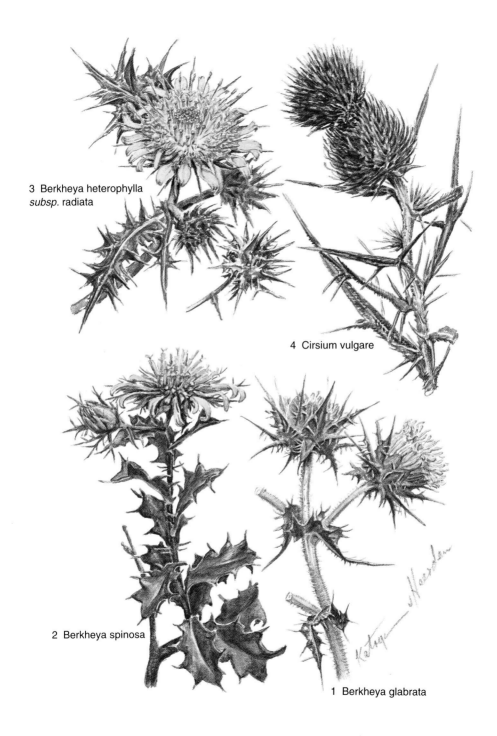

3 Berkheya heterophylla
subsp. radiata

4 Cirsium vulgare

2 Berkheya spinosa

1 Berkheya glabrata

ASTERACEAE

1 **Artemisa afra**   wormwood, wilde-als   **
Much-branched shrub up to 1 m. Alternate leaves deeply divided and covered with
fine white hairs on underside. Inflorescence an extended panicle with individual
yellow flowers. Used medicinally since time immemorial, particularly as an
anthelmintic, tonic and tincture. Hardly grazed.

Great Escarpment; Upper, Great and Little Karoo; southwestern, southern, eastern and northern Cape; Lesotho, Namibia and Swaziland in permanent and seasonal streams and flood plains.

2 **Conyza scabrida**   oven bush, oondbos   **
Shrub up to 2 m along river banks. In early summer masses of small yellow flower-
heads appear to cover the plant. Leaves alternate, serrated and with an unpleasant
smell. Used by early settlers for dusting out their ovens. From this practice came
the superstition that bread baked in an oven that had not been cleaned with a twig
of this plant would not rise. Infusions were widely used during the 1918 'flu epi-
demic. Hardly grazed, but is nonetheless useful in stabilizing banks of rivers during floods. Namaqualand; Great Escarpment; Upper, Great and Little Karoo; Cape
Fold Belt; southwestern, southern and eastern Cape; Orange Free State; Natal;
Transvaal; Botswana, Lesotho, Namibia, Swaziland and Zimbabwe in permanent
and seasonal streams, flood plains and mountain slopes.

3 **Cuspidia cernua**   wortelbossie   **
Annual up to 30 cm, covered with soft spines. Flowers yellow. Ripe seed does not
fall out of the fruiting head, but germinates within this protection, sending taproots
through the scales. Grazed.

Namaqualand; Great Escarpment; Upper, Great and Little Karoo and eastern
Cape in flats, apron veld, rante, mountain slopes and disturbed areas.

4 **Dicoma spinosa**   karmedik   ***
Shrub to 25 cm, covered in long, very sharp spines. Oval leaves blue-green. Lilac
and white flowers are about 30 mm in diameter and resemble those of an everlast-
ing. Well grazed by some species of smallstock, particularly goats.

Great Escarpment; Great and Little Karoo; southwestern and southern Cape in
mountain slopes and rante.

5 **Dimorphotheca cuneata**   white bietou, weather prophet, witbietou   *
Common shrub up to 70 cm. Toothed leaves are opposite and aromatic. Disc florets
yellow, ray florets pure white above and a coppery colour below. Flowers close in
the afternoon and do not open again till the following morning. Not much grazed,
can poison animals because of large amounts of prussic acid present.

Namaqualand; Bushmanland; Great Escarpment; Upper, Great and Little Karoo;
Cape Fold Belt; southwestern, southern, eastern and northern Cape; Orange Free
State and Botswana in flats, apron veld, mountain slopes, crowns and rante.

6 **Phymaspermum** sp.   ***
Shrub up to 65 cm. Covered with white flowers that are particularly noticeable at
midday. Well grazed.

Great Escarpment on mountain slopes.

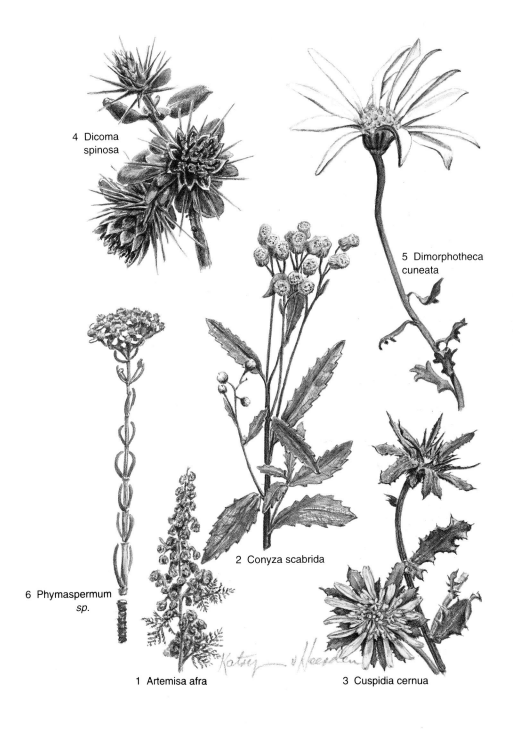

4 Dicoma spinosa

5 Dimorphotheca cuneata

6 Phymaspermum *sp.*

2 Conyza scabrida

1 Artemisa afra

3 Cuspidia cernua

ASTERACEAE

1 **Chrysanthemoides incana**   bietou   ****
Large shrub up to 2,5 m with diameter of up to 8 m if given the opportunity, soil and adequate water. A variable species that is very well grazed.

Namaqualand; Great Escarpment; Great Karoo; southwestern and southern Cape and Namibia in permanent and seasonal streams, flood plains, flats and kloofs.

2 **Eriocephalus decussatus**   doringkapok   **
Shrub up to 45 cm. Branches end in spikes. Usually occurs in flat areas that have been disturbed or overgrazed. Not much grazed.

Namaqualand; Bushmanland; Great Escarpment; Upper and Great Karoo and eastern Cape in flats and rante.

3 **Eriocephalus ericoides**   kapok bush, gewonekapok   **
Very common shrub growing at times to almost 1 m. Leaves small, narrow and usually opposite. Flowers insignificant. White, wooly 'kapok' surrounding the seed is very characteristic. This 'kapok' is sometimes brownish. Not very palatable, and is susceptible to attack by Karoo caterpillar.

Widespread throughout southern Africa in a wide variety of habitats.

4 **Eriocephalus punctulatus**   boegoekapok   **
Large shrub reaching 75 cm. Fleshy leaves can be both opposite and alternate. Leaves used as a boegoe substitute. Grazed to some extent.

Namaqualand; Great Escarpment; Upper, Great and Little Karoo; southwestern and eastern Cape in rante and mountain slopes.

5 **Eriocephalus spinescens**   doringkapok   **
Very common shrub usually not exceeding 60 cm. Much resembles *Eriocephalus ericoides* except that leaves are sparser and stems have terminal spikes. Seed fibres are sometimes brownish. Even less palatable than *Eriocephalus ericoides*.

Great Escarpment; Upper and Great Karoo; southwestern and northern Cape and Orange Free State in flats, apron veld, rante, mountain slopes and disturbed areas.

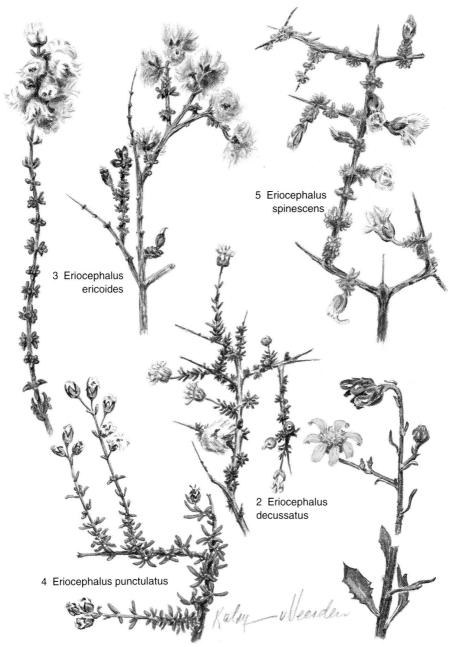

3 Eriocephalus
ericoides

5 Eriocephalus
spinescens

2 Eriocephalus
decussatus

4 Eriocephalus punctulatus

1 Chrysanthemoides incana

ASTERACEAE
Euryops species
In early days a special 'resin soap' made from *Euryops* species, was prized as very good, as was the resin collected from almost all these plants. Some bigger, and more unpalatable *Euryops* species were chopped out at great expense to make place for more palatable plants. All members of this genus have yellow ray and disc florets.

1 **Euryops annae**   waterharpuis, wildeharpuisbos   **
[=Euryops oligoglossus]
Shrub up to 50 cm. Leaves are small, narrow with a strong astringent smell. Animals graze flower heads readily, but bushy parts are not at all palatable.
   Great Escarpment; Upper, Great and Little Karoo; southwestern, southern and eastern Cape and Lesotho near water, in seasonal streams, mountain slopes, kloofs and crowns.

2 **Euryops imbricatus**   resin bush, harpuisbos   **
Large shrub reaching 1 m. Leaves are shiny, dark green and narrow. Flowers a brilliant yellow. A fairly useless bush to the stock farmer except as ground cover. When it grows in dense stands with rhinoceros bush (*Elytropappus rhinocerotis*), it can become a fire hazard as it burns easily even when green. Not grazed.
   Great Escarpment; Upper and Little Karoo and Cape Fold Belt in flats, rante, mountain slopes, kloofs and crowns.

3 **Euryops lateriflorus**   vetharpuis   **
Shrub having fewer branches than most *Euryops* species, and up to 1,2 m. Leaves overlap and are arranged symmetrically. Like others, flowers are grazed, but the bush itself is hardly touched by livestock.
   Namaqualand; Bushmanland; Great Escarpment; Northern, Upper, Great, Tanqua and Little Karoo; southwestern, southern and eastern Cape; Orange Free State and Namibia in a wide variety of habitats.

4 **Euryops nodosus**   **
Shrub up to 70 cm. Not much grazed except, perhaps for the flowers.
   Great Escarpment; Upper Karoo and eastern Cape in rante, mountain slopes and kloofs.

5 **Euryops subcarnosus** subsp. **vulgaris**   soetharpuis   **
Shrub up to 65 cm. Small, narrow light-green leaves. Plants are covered with masses of yellow, daisy-like flowers that give off a strong, pleasant aroma after good rains. Resin exudes from the stem, and in earlier days was collected and sold. Animals graze flowers eagerly, but the plant is not otherwise used to any great extent. During flowering time it is not unusual to see sheep with yellow stained mouths from grazing flowers. Namaqualand; Bushmanland; Great Escarpment; Northern, Upper, Great and Little Karoo; southwestern, southern, eastern and northern Cape and Namibia in seasonal streams, flats, apron veld, rante and slopes.

6 **Hertia cluytiifolia**   ertjiebos   **
Much-branched shrub up to 70 cm. Leaves spade-shaped. Flowers yellow. Resembles members of the genus *Euryops*. Not very palatable. Great Escarpment; Upper and Great Karoo and Namibia in flats, rante and disturbed areas.

158

1 Euryops annae

4 Euryops
nodosus

5
Euryops subcarnosus
subsp. vulgaris

3 Euryops
lateriflorus

2 Euryops imbricatus

6 Hertia cluytiifolia

ASTERACEAE

1 Felicia fascicularis bloublommetjieskaroo ****
Dwarf shrub to 25 cm. Flower-heads with lilac ray and yellow disc florets. Leaves very small. The well-known 'bloublommetjieskaroo' of literature. It seems to have been more common before our present grazing practices all but exterminated it. Very palatable to all types of herbivores. Great Escarpment; Upper, Great and Little Karoo; southwestern, southern, eastern and northern Cape; Orange Free State; Transvaal and Namibia in flats, apron veld, rante and mountain slopes.

2 Felicia filifolia ghombos, persbergdraaibos * or **
Shrub to 60 cm. Very showy with its mass of flowerheads with blue to lilac ray and yellow disc florets. Now regarded as an invasive bush that has spread at a disquieting rate into both the Transkei and Free State. In some areas regarded as reasonably palatable, but poisonous in others. Namaqualand; Great Escarpment; Northern, Upper, Great and Little Karoo; southwestern, southern, eastern and northern Cape; Orange Free State; Transvaal; Lesotho and Namibia in seasonal streams, flats, apron veld, rante, mountain slopes and kloofs.

3 Felicia hirsuta bloublommetjie ****
Dwarf shrub to 20 cm. Flowers much resemble other *Felicia* species, but generally smaller. They appear to change colour like those of *Felicia muricata*. Well grazed, and before its drastic reduction through overgrazing, was one of the more palatable plants of this area. Namaqualand; Bushmanland; Great Escarpment; Upper, Great and Little Karoo; southern, eastern and northern Cape; Orange Free State and Namibia in seasonal streams and a wide range of habitats.

4 Felicia muricata bloublommetjie ****
Shrub to 20 cm. Flowers appear yellow in the morning and blue later in the day because ray florets fold behind the yellow disc florets at night, only reappearing during sunlight hours. Used by some Black tribes to obtain confessions from suspects by putting small pieces in their food, and as a remedy for sick cattle. Germinates well, but large numbers die during a prolonged drought. Well grazed, and is a sought-after bush. Widespread throughout southern Africa in a wide range of habitats.

5 Felicia namaquana bloublommetjie-opslag ***
Annual seldom exceeding 15 cm. Leaves larger than either of the preceding two species. Flowers much resembles theirs, although a white-flowering specimen has been found. Germinates very well, and appears in great numbers after rains. Because of numbers, it gives a good amount of feed. Well grazed.
   Namaqualand; Bushmanland; Great Escarpment; Northern, Upper, Great and Tanqua Karoo; southwestern and northern Cape and Namibia in seasonal streams, flood plains, flats, apron veld, rante and disturbed areas.

6 Felicia ovata grootbloublommetjie *****
Shrub to 40 cm. Stems rangy. Dark green, hairy leaves. Flowers dark blue to lilac rays and yellow discs. Seeds freely, and increases well in spared veld. Fairly drought resistant. Frequently shelters inside other plants. Very eagerly grazed by all herbivores. Namaqualand; Great Escarpment; Northern, Upper, Great and Little Karoo; southwestern, southern, eastern and northern Cape and Orange Free State in apron veld, rante, mountain slopes, kloofs and crowns.

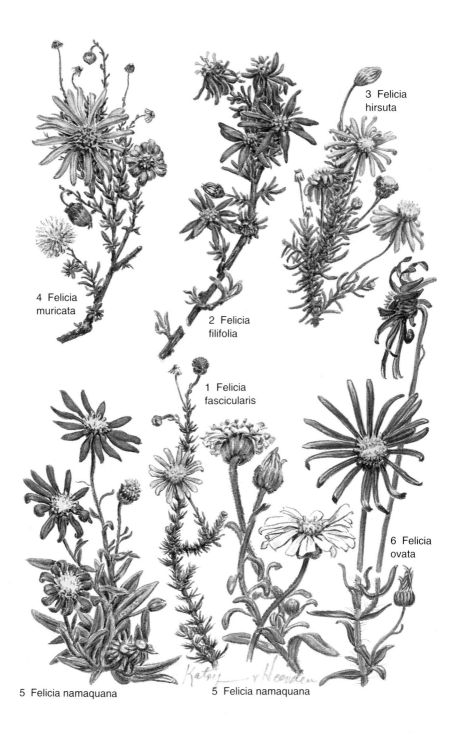

3 Felicia hirsuta

4 Felicia muricata

2 Felicia filifolia

1 Felicia fascicularis

6 Felicia ovata

5 Felicia namaquana

5 Felicia namaquana

ASTERACEAE

1 **Helichrysum pumilio** subsp. **pumilio**   sewejaartjie, wolbossie   **

Shrublet 2-20 cm high. Young stems hairy, older stems brown and lignified. Leaves white-woolley. Grazed, but never contributes very much to total amount ingested.

Namaqualand; Bushmanland; Great Escarpment; Northern, Upper and Great Karoo; Cape Fold Belt; eastern Cape; Orange Free State in gravel, at base of rocks and in stream beds in apron veld, rante and mountain slopes.

2 & 3 **Helichrysum rosum**. var. **arcuatum**   bergankerkaroo   ****

Shrub 50 cm. Can be mat-forming and often creeps under other bushes. Slightly hairy branches. Stems noticeable for formation of 'anchors'. Very hardy, and germination good. Often confused with *Helichrysum dregeanum* which does not occur in the Karoo, as it has the same growth habit. Very palatable, though less so where large numbers occur. Great Escarpment; Upper and Great Karoo; eastern Cape and Orange Free State in apron veld, rante, mountain slopes, kloofs and crowns.

4 **Helichrysum lucilioides**   bergkerriebos   ***

Shrub up to 50 cm. Thick, woody base. Leaves small, alternate, simple, silvery grey-green and usually packed on outside of plant; when crushed they smell of curry. Unobtrusive flowers vary from pink through yellow to white. Very drought resistant; at such times leaves turn grey-brown and fold up. Very well grazed on apron veld, but not palatable where soil is brack. Namaqualand; Great Escarpment; Northern, Upper and Great Karoo; eastern and northern Cape; Orange Free State and Namibia in rante, mountain slopes and crowns.

5 **Helichrysum trilineatum**   **

Shrub up to 90 cm. Old branches bare and rough; new growth greyish-white and woolly. Leaves have recurved tips. Often forms large colonies on mountain slopes. Not grazed much. Great Escarpment; Upper and Great Karoo; eastern Cape; Orange Free State; Natal and Lesotho in mountain slopes and crowns.

6 **Helichrysum zeyheri**   vaalbergkaroo   ***

Shrub to 60 cm. Overall greyish colour. Usually compact at base, but has many thin stems. Leaves sparse, grey-green to blue-green. Inflorescences consist of many pink flowers that turn white with age. Very noticeable in full flower, but insignificant after blooms have passed. Grazed.

Widespread throughout southern Africa in a wide range of habitats.

7 **Helichrysum scitulum**   **

Uncommon shrub or creeper of mountain tops. May have a diameter of 35 cm. Flower deep pink and white. Not grazed. Great Escarpment (Nieuweveld, Renosterberg, Bamboesberg, Stormberg and Witteberg near Lady Grey) on crowns.

8 **Phymaspermum parvifolium**   good Karoo, galsteenbossie, witheuningkaroo,
                                 witblommetjie   ****

Dwarf shrub with many branches. When in flower it's covered with white-rayed flowers that attract bees in great numbers. Exceptionally drought-resistant. Very well grazed by all livestock. Great Escarpment; Upper, Great and Little Karoo; eastern Cape and Orange Free State in flats.

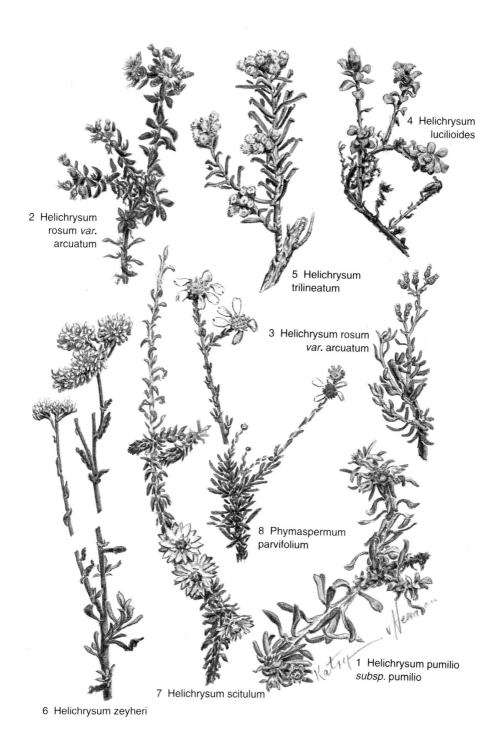

2 Helichrysum rosum *var.* arcuatum

5 Helichrysum trilineatum

4 Helichrysum lucilioides

3 Helichrysum rosum *var.* arcuatum

8 Phymaspermum parvifolium

1 Helichrysum pumilio *subsp.* pumilio

7 Helichrysum scitulum

6 Helichrysum zeyheri

ASTERACEAE

1 Cotula coronopifolia   gansgras   **

Herb to 35 cm. Stems often decumbent as they often do not have the strength to remain up straight unless supported. Flowers in yellow balls. Not grazed, but geese are fond of them. Widespread throughout southern Africa in permanent streams and other wet places.

2 Elytropappus rhinocerotis   rhinoceros bush, renosterbos   *

Shrub to 1,5 m. Foliage resembles cypress. Leaves narrow, grey-green, up to 1,2 cm long, closely packed on stems. Insignificant brown flowers very small. Shrub has overall brownish appearance in summer. Forms fire hazard when occurring in dense patches as it burns easily even when green. Spread terrifically since first recorded by Van Riebeeck in 1652. No satisfactory reason has yet been given for this. A local superstition is that the Karoo paralysis tick (*Ixodes rubicundus*) is not poisonous in veld that does not contain rhinoceros bush. Widely used medicinally, also as a cure for krimpsiekte in sheep. Not grazed. Widespread throughout southern Africa in wide range of habitats, though mostly in mountains.

3 Garuleum bipinnatum   slanghoutjie, kowerbos   *****

Shrub to 50 cm. Stems light grey. Leaves light green, small and narrow. Daisy-like flowers usually have white, though sometimes blue to lilac rays, with yellow disc florets. Early settlers prized the root as a snakebite remedy. Has also been used as a cure for various chest diseases and a mouthwash. The root has a digitalis action. Though not as palatable as koggelmandervoetkaroo (*Limeum aethiopicum*), it provides a large quantity of very high quality feed.

   Namaqualand; Great Escarpment; Upper, Great and Little Karoo and Cape Fold Belt in apron veld, rante, mountain slopes and kloofs.

4 Geigeria filifolia   vermeerbos   *

Annual growing on perennial rootstock. Seldom exceeds 15 cm. Leaves long and narrow. Flowers yellow. Stems short. Grazing this plant may cause paralysis of oesophagus, which leads to regurgitation and in severe cases rumen entering trachea and causing pneumonia. Losses very severe in some years.

   Great Escarpment; Northern, Upper and Great Karoo; southwestern, eastern and northern Cape; Orange Free State; Natal; Transvaal; Botswana and Lesotho in flood plains, flats, apron veld and mountain slopes.

5 Hirpicium alienatum   haarbossie, meerjarige gousblom   ***

Shrub seldom exceeding 50 cm. Linear leaves tipped with small spines. Both disc and ray florets yellow above. Ray florets brownish below. Involucral bracts appear to be covered with spines. Palatable. Namaqualand; Bushmanland; Great Escarpment; Upper, Great and Little Karoo; Cape Fold Belt; southwestern and southern Cape and Namibia in rante, mountain slopes and crowns.

6 Ifloga glomerata   bekvol   **

Shrublet looks like floral equivalent of Tom Thumb. Seldom reaches more than 7 cm. Leaves long, narrow and packed round stem. Flowers insignificant. Not grazed. Namaqualand; Great Escarpment; Northern, Upper and Great Karoo; southern, eastern and northern Cape; Orange Free State and Namibia in seasonal streams, flats and disturbed areas.

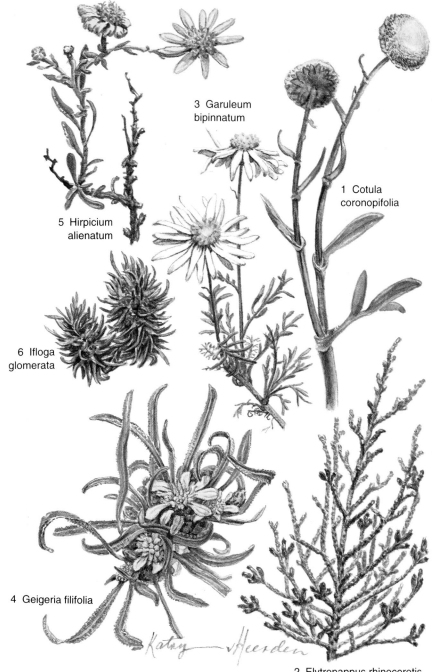

3 Garuleum
bipinnatum

1 Cotula
coronopifolia

5 Hirpicium
alienatum

6 Ifloga
glomerata

4 Geigeria filifolia

2 Elytropappus rhinocerotis

ASTERACEAE

1 **Arctotis adpressa** gousblom **

Stemless perennial restricted to Roggeveld and Nieuweveld ranges. Grazed to a limited extent.

Great Escarpment near Calvinia, Sutherland and Beaufort West on crowns in heavy clay.

2 **Trichogyne decumbens** **

[=Ifloga decumbens]

Shrub to 15 cm. White flowers in bunches on ends of short stems. Not grazed.

Great Escarpment; Great and Little Karoo; Orange Free State and Lesotho on slopes and crowns.

3 **Osteospermum microphyllum** wolfolie **

Evergreen shrub to 40 cm. Leaves linear. Woody stems erect. Yellow flowers smaller than those of other species. Not much grazed.

Namaqualand; Great Escarpment; Upper and Great Karoo; southwestern and northern Cape; Botswana and Namibia in apron veld, rante and mountain slopes.

4 **Osteospermum scariosum** bietou *****

Dwarf herb up to 30 cm. Semi-succulent leaves alternate and resemble those of *Osteospermum sinuatum*. Flowers borne on leafless branches. Seed is winged. Very drought resistant and responds well to rain. When wilted level of prussic acid may cause deaths among sheep and goats. Exceptionally well grazed.

Widespread throughout southern Africa except Namaqualand in flood plains, flats, apron veld, rante and mountain slopes.

5 **Osteospermum sinuatum** bietou *****

Shrub reaching 80 cm, though usually grazed down to about 20 cm. Stems whitish. Leaves semi-succulent, opposite and serrated. Flowers yellow. Seed winged. Very drought resistant, and responds well to rain. May cause deaths from prussic acid poisoning when wilted. Grow best in shelter of larger bushes as they are very palatable.

Widespread throughout southern Africa in flood plains, flats, apron veld, rante, mountain slopes and crowns.

6 **Osteospermum spinescens** rivierdraaibos ****

Robust, bushy shrub up to 120 cm. Usually as wide as high. Stems often twisted and light grey. Alternate leaves have three lobes (or sometimes teeth). Has exceptionally strong root system and is able to withstand very severe droughts. Well grazed.

Widespread throughout southern Africa in seasonal streams, flood plains and rante.

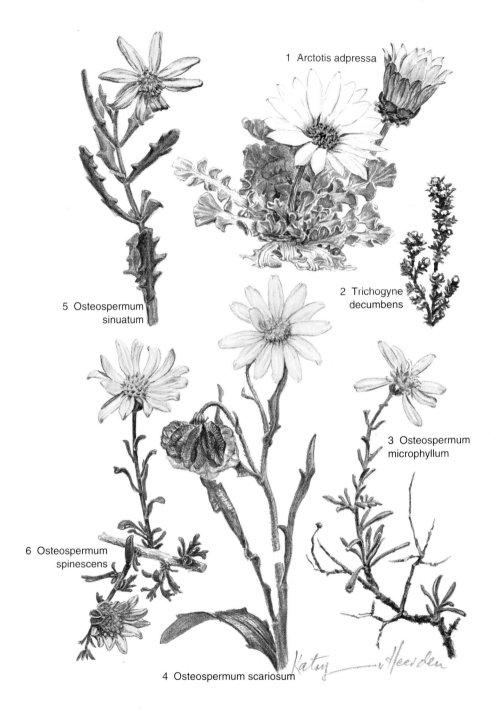

1 Arctotis adpressa

2 Trichogyne decumbens

5 Osteospermum sinuatum

3 Osteospermum microphyllum

6 Osteospermum spinescens

4 Osteospermum scariosum

ASTERACEAE

1 **Arctotheca calendula**   Cape marigold, tonteldoek, soetgousblom   **

Annual up to 25 cm. Leaves rough above and white-woolly below. Flower stalks slightly hairy. Not a strong grower, but a nuisance in vineyards and wheat fields. Grazed, but does not provide much feed.

Widespread throughout southern Africa in disturbed areas.

2 **Othonna pavonia**   **

Shrub up to 60 cm. Stems reddish. Flowers yellow. Leaves very deeply lobed, resembling the tines of a rake. Hardly grazed.

Namaqualand; Great Escarpment; Upper and Great Karoo; southwestern and eastern Cape on mountain slopes.

3 **Othonna sedifolia**   ****

Smallish shrub. Semi-succulent leaves. Well grazed by all livestock.

Namaqualand; Bushmanland; Great Escarpment; Great Karoo and Namibia in apron veld, rante and mountain slopes.

4 **Senecio acutifolius**   **

Shrub reaching 45 cm. Flowers yellow. Slightly fleshy leaves pointed. Grazed.

Great Escarpment and Great Karoo in apron veld, rante and mountain slopes.

5 **Pegolettia retrofracta**   perdebos, geelbergdraaibos   ***

Shrub up to 90 cm. Small leaves alternate. Flowers yellow. Leaves, when crushed, smell of apples. Well grazed.

Namaqualand; Bushmanland; Great Escarpment; Northern, Upper and Great Karoo; southwestern, eastern and northern Cape; Orange Free State; Transvaal and Namibia in rante and mountain slopes.

6 **Senecio erysimoides**   **

Herb up to 50 cm. Very deeply lobed leaves give plant a lacy appearance. Flowers yellow. Not grazed.

Bushmanland; Great Escarpment; Tanqua Karoo and Namibia on crowns.

7 **Senecio harveianus**   **

Herb up to 80 cm. Long, linear leaves grow in bunches. Flowers yellow and numbers occur on ends of long stems. Not grazed.

Great Escarpment; Northern and Little Karoo and eastern Cape in kloofs and crowns.

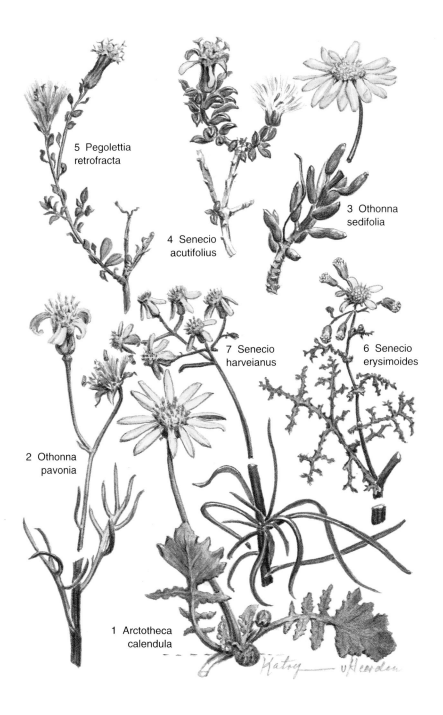

5 Pegolettia
retrofracta

4 Senecio
acutifolius

3 Othonna
sedifolia

7 Senecio
harveianus

6 Senecio
erysimoides

2 Othonna
pavonia

1 Arctotheca
calendula

ASTERACEAE

1 **Pentzia globosa**   vaalkaroo, vleikaroo   **

Very common shrub to 50 cm. Resembles *Pentzia incana* superficially, but stems do not strike down and form roots. Has taken over much good veld, especially grass veld, and is often used as an indicator of high potential veld. Has been used medicinally for convulsions, fevers and typhoid. It is ironic that despite its high feed value, it is hardly grazed because of its unpalatability.

Great Escarpment; Northern and Upper Karoo; southwestern, eastern and northern Cape; Orange Free State; Transvaal; Botswana and Lesotho in seasonal streams, flats, pans and crowns.

2 **Pentzia incana**   anchor Karoo, ankerkaroo   ***

Very common shrub to 50 cm, though grazing practices usually keep it down to about 25 cm. Flowers small round balls. Leaves grey-green, small, alternate and have a bitter, pungent smell, so characteristic of the Karoo. Long shoots that form during a good season strike down and form new bushes. The plant known as 'vleikaroo' has much smaller flowers. It does not strike down, and is not at all palatable. Main host of Karoo caterpillar (*Loxostege frustalis*). May look drought-stricken even in a good season because of this. A dry twig with leaves attached submerged completely in water in the sun for a day, will start to show greenness on its leaves by the following morning. Has been used medicinally for the relief of stomach complaints, and chewing young stems give relief in cases of toothache. Keeping this plant grazed short may lead to veld deterioration if the degree of 'shortness' is too severe. A staple feed of animals on most farms. Although common, it is not of high quality and needs to be replaced by something better.

Widespread throughout southern Africa in wide range of habitats.

3 **Pentzia punctata**   beeskaroo   **

Rigid, bushy shrub up to 60 cm. Leaves alternate. Flowers borne on longish stalks that have leaves to their tops. Grazed, especially by cattle, during summer.

Great Escarpment; Northern, Upper and Great Karoo; northern Cape and Orange Free State in mountain slopes, kloofs and crowns.

4 **Pentzia quinquefida**   ***

Shrub up to 45 cm. Often mistaken for *Pentzia sphaerocephala*. Yellow flowers borne on long stems with no leaflets. Well grazed, but seldom found in large numbers.

Great Escarpment; Upper and Great Karoo; eastern and northern Cape and Orange Free State in seasonal streams, rante, mountain slopes, kloofs and crowns.

5 **Pentzia spinescens**   witstamkaroo, doringkaroo   ****

Shrub reaching 45 cm. Stems white. Leaves small, narrow. Flower-heads bigger than those of *Pentzia incana*. A favourite host of the Karoo caterpillar (*Loxostege frustalis*). Very well grazed and only its susceptibility to caterpillar attack prevents it being classed among the best plants. Namaqualand; Bushmanland; Great Escarpment; Northern, Upper and Great Karoo; northern Cape; Orange Free State; Transvaal; Botswana and Namibia in seasonal streams, flood plains, flats and rante.

6 **Ursinia nana**   **

Small annual. Flowers yellow. Appears in its thousands if conditions are right. Grazed, but only to a limited degree. Ants very fond of carrying seed to their nests.

Widespread throughout southern Africa in flats, apron veld and disturbed areas.

170

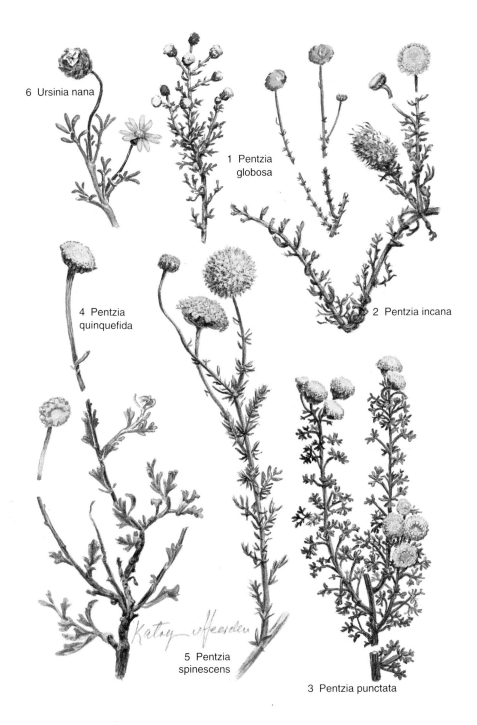

6 Ursinia nana

1 Pentzia globosa

2 Pentzia incana

4 Pentzia quinquefida

5 Pentzia spinescens

3 Pentzia punctata

Katey van Heerden

ASTERACEAE

1 Chrysocoma ciliata   bitterbos   **
[=Chrysocoma tenuifolia]
Very common shrub to 30 cm. Narrow, olive-green leaves are bitter and give certain areas a greenish look. Small yellow flowers. Is not drought resistant, but recovers quickly, especially if grazing system is not good. Very active pioneer bush, and is often regarded as an indicator of poor grazing systems. Has been widely used medicinally. Not readily grazed, but where pregnant animals eat it through lack of other feed, lambs may suffer from alopecia (kaalsiekte), where the lamb, but not the ewe, looses its wool or hair. More prevalent in goats as they eat more than sheep. Widespread throughout southern Africa in wide range of habitats.

2 Oncosiphon pilulifera   stinkkruid   **
[=Pentzia pilulifera]
Herb to 30 cm. Leaves lacy with a very strong smell if even slightly crushed. Flowers yellow pom-poms. Not grazed. Widespread throughout southern Africa in permanent and seasonal streams and disturbed areas.

3 Pentzia sphaerocephala;   grootberggansieskaroo   ****
Shrub to 60 cm. Differs from *Pentzia incana* with larger flower heads on long leafless stems, and leaves generally larger. Also has characteristic smell, though not as strong. A major host of Karoo caterpillar (*Loxostege frustalis*), and is one of the first to be invaded. Well grazed. Namaqualand; Great Escarpment; Upper, Great and Little Karoo; southern and eastern Cape; Orange Free State and Namibia in seasonal streams, flats, rante, mountain slopes, kloofs and crowns.

4 Phymaspermum aciculare   heuningkaroo   ***
Shrub up to 60 cm. White flowers particularly noticeable at midday. Well grazed.
   Great Escarpment; Northern, Upper and Little Karoo; southern Cape; Orange Free State; Transvaal and Namibia in rante, mountain slopes and kloofs.

5 Phymaspermum schroteri   heuningkaroo   ****
Shrub up to 50 cm. Covered in white, daisy-like flowers after good rains. Very palatable, and can provide lots of grazable material.
   Great Escarpment and Great Karoo in rante, mountain slopes and kloofs.

6 Pteronia erythrochaeta   **
Shrub reaching 50 cm. Unusual feathery pink flowers. Not very palatable, but provides a certain amount of feed. Northern and Upper Karoo; northern Cape and Botswana in flood plains, flats and rante.

7 Pteronia glomerata   perdebossie, gombos   **
Shrub to 60 cm. Usually twice as broad as high. Branches dark, erect, for thin. Buds covered by a thin waxy layer as protection from cold winter winds. Not grazed.
   Great Escarpment; Northern, Upper, Great, Tanqua and Little Karoo; Cape Fold Belt and southwestern Cape in apron veldand rante.

8 Rosenia glandulosa   klierbos   **
Shrub to 45 cm. Buds like small pineapples. Leaves opposite, whorled. Only slightly grazed. Great Escarpment west of Beaufort West on crowns, usually in heavy clay.

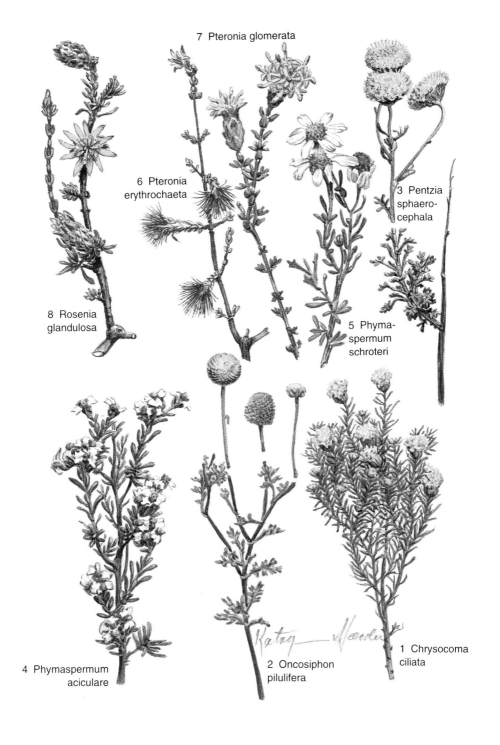

7 Pteronia glomerata

6 Pteronia
erythrochaeta

3 Pentzia
sphaero-
cephala

8 Rosenia
glandulosa

5 Phyma-
spermum
schroteri

4 Phymaspermum
aciculare

2 Oncosiphon
pilulifera

1 Chrysocoma
ciliata

ASTERACEAE
1 **Pteronia adenocarpa** boegoekaroo   **
Shrub to 60 cm. Twigs often opposite and plant rigid. Leaves opposite. Flower heads very sticky. Bright pink buds open to waxy white flowers. Regrowth slow. Although few seedlings found, it is very hardy. A very old Khoisan buchu remedy. Grazed, but usually only under pressure.

   Great Escarpment; Northern, Upper, Great and Little Karoo; southern and eastern Cape in flats and rante.

2 **Pteronia glauca** geelboegoekaroo, perdekaroo   **
Shrub to 80 cm. Long, lax stems. Usually wider than high. Like *Pentzia incana* it propagates by shoots striking root. Young parts often hairy. Leaves narrow and opposite. Flowers smaller than others of this family, and always longer than broad. Remarkable for general grey-green or blue-green colour. Usually flowers in early spring. Hardly grazed.

   Namaqualand; Bushmanland; Great Escarpment; Upper, Great and Little Karoo eastern and northern Cape; Orange Free State and Namibia in seasonal streams, flood plains, flats, rante and kloofs.

3 **Pteronia paniculata** gombossie   **
Aromatic bushy shrub to 50 cm. Leaves dark green. Flowers bright yellow. At times multiplies in patches on slopes of mountains. These show up as dark green clumps. Not grazed.

   Namaqualand; Bushmanland; Great Escarpment; Upper, Great and Little Karoo; Cape Fold Belt; southwestern, southern, eastern and northern Cape and Namibia in rante and mountain slopes.

4 **Pteronia mucronata** kersbossie   **
Very sticky flowers. Not very palatable
   Great Escarpment in rante.

5 **Pteronia staehelinoides**   **
Shrub to 50 cm. Flowers sticky. Not very palatable.
   Great Escarpment; Great and Little Karoo; southern and eastern Cape in flats, rante and disturbed areas.

6 **Pteronia viscosa** gombossie   **
Shrub to 50 cm. Flowers sticky. Not well grazed, though animals do take it when forced.
   Great Escarpment; Upper, Great and Little Karoo and eastern Cape in flats, apron veld and rante.

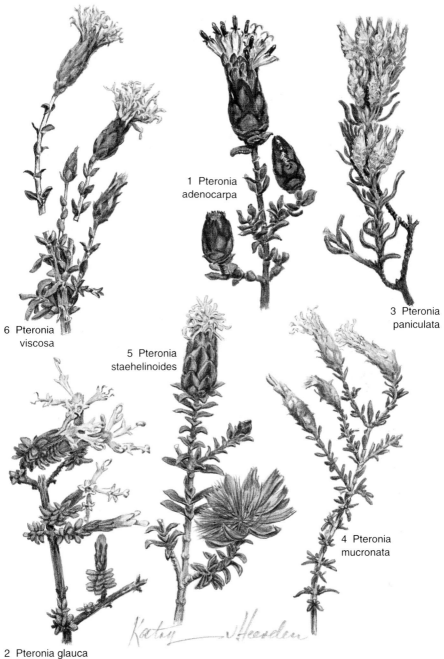

1 Pteronia
adenocarpa

3 Pteronia
paniculata

6 Pteronia
viscosa

5 Pteronia
staehelinoides

4 Pteronia
mucronata

2 Pteronia glauca

ASTERACEAE

1 **Rosenia humilis**   perdekaroo, hartebeeskaroo   **

Hardy shrub to 40 cm. May be identified by previous season's buds resembling small pineapples that often cover it. Stems woody and grey to greyish-white. Leaves light green, often with a bluish tinge and becoming grey-blue as the plant ages. They are long, narrow, bunched and covered with fine hairs, more abundantly on young plants. Young leaves have pleasant pine aroma. Yellow ray and disc florets. Buds golden-brown to dark brown; sticky when green. Does not appear to be very susceptible to Karoo caterpillar (*Loxostege frustalis*). Very drought resistant, and provides feed when most other plants have been grazed. Not very palatable.

Widespread throughout the arid areas of southern Africa except Namaqualand in flats, apron veld, rante and mountain slopes.

2 **Rosenia oppositifolia**   blouperdekaroo   ***

Shrub up to 70 cm. Has a general bluish-grey appearance. Leaves small, though they may vary in size. Flowers yellow. Fairly well grazed.

Great Escarpment; Upper and Great Karoo; southwestern and eastern Cape in flats, rante and crowns.

3 **Senecio achilleifolius**   slootopdammer   ***

Shrub up to 50 cm, though usually much lower as the thickish, prostrate stems root very easily. This causes it to cover a large area, making it useful in arresting erosion. Stems reddish. Flowers yellow. Well grazed, and should be rested if needed to combat erosion.

Namaqualand; Great Escarpment; Upper, Great and Tanqua Karoo; Cape Fold Belt; southwestern and eastern Cape; Orange Free State; Natal and Transvaal in permanent and seasonal streams, flood plains and mountain slopes.

4 **Kleinia longiflora**   sjambokbos   **
[=*Senecio longiflorus*]

Shrub up to 1m. A striking sight when in seed with its tuft of long-haired, white seeds topping each branch. Can be confused with *Euphorbia* species when not in flower or seed, but no white latex issues from stems. Has been used for making snuff. Grazed at times, though not always so.

Namaqualand; Great Escarpment; Northern, Upper, Great and Little Karoo; Cape Fold Belt; northern Cape; Orange Free State; Transvaal; Botswana and Namibia in apron veld, rante and mountain slopes.

5 **Senecio radicans**   bokkos   ***

Prostrate herb with perennial rootstock. Alternate leaves are succulent. Flowers borne on upright leafless branches. If not grazed, will ramble through many other species of plants covering up to a square meter. Well grazed by sheep and goats, but not much feed on any single plant.

Great Escarpment; Upper, Great and Little Karoo; southwestern, southern, eastern and northern Cape; Orange Free State and Transvaal inside bushes in apron veld, rante and mountain slopes.

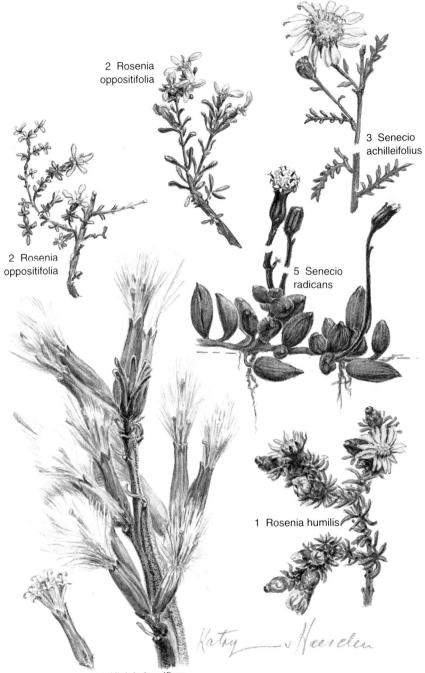

2 Rosenia
oppositifolia

3 Senecio
achilleifolius

2 Rosenia
oppositifolia

5 Senecio
radicans

1 Rosenia humilis

4 Kleinia longiflora

ASTERACEAE

1 **Cichorium intybus**   chicory, sigorei   **

Exotic shrub, originally from Europe and Asia. Erect and woody, up to 1 m. Milky sap, very strong taproot. Roasted root used as replacement or addition to coffee. Hardly grazed. Great Escarpment; Upper Karoo; Great and Little Karoo; southwestern, southern, eastern and northern Cape; Orange Free State and Transvaal in disturbed areas.

2 **Pseudognaphalium undulatum**   cudweed, groenbossie   **

Spreading annual herb to 60 cm. Stems greyish-white. Leaves' upper sides green, drying brown, while lower sides are white-felted. Not grazed.

Great Escarpment; Upper, Great and Little Karoo; southwestern, southern and eastern Cape; Orange Free State; Natal; Transvaal; Lesotho and Namibia in permanent and seasonal streams, rante, mountain slopes and disturbed areas.

3 **Pteronia pallens**   Scholtzbos, armoedsbos   *

Perennial shrub to 50cm. Stems whitish. Leaves opposite, narrow. Florets slightly sticky, yellow to orange. Young growth bright green. When grazed the animal may show signs of weakness, apathy and jaundice as it contains a liver poison.

Namaqualand; Upper, Great, Tanqua and Little Karoo; southwestern, southern and northern Cape in flats, rante and mountain slopes.

4 **Tarchonanthus camphoratus**   camphor tree, vaalbos   ***

Small tree to 9 m. Alternate leaves smell strongly of camphor, though it does not appear to contain any. Splinters can cause festering sores. Timber takes a good polish and has been used for making musical instruments, boats and furniture. Stems make very durable posts. Leaves have been smoked as tobacco substitute, and it is supposed to have been slightly narcotic. Widely used medicinally for complaints as varied as headaches and plague. The seedheads are also used for making aromatic sachets. Grazed by most livestock.

Widespread throughout southern Africa in seasonal streams, mountain slopes, kloofs and crowns.

5 **Vellereophyton niveum**   **

White-woolly herb 10 cm. Usually prostrate to weakly erect with many stems of varying length issuing from crown. Roots may be perennial. Distinguished from *Vellerophytum dealbatum* by broader heads and slight red colouring in flower. Not grazed. Great Escarpment; Great Karoo in permanent streams and other wet areas

6 **Xanthium spinosum**   burrweed, boetebossie   *

Exotic to 1,2 m, originally from South America, though probably introduced from Europe and collected here in 1690's. Much-branched herb now regarded as a cosmopolitan weed. Alternate leaves long, usually three-lobed. Fruits contained in burs about 1cm long, change from green to yellow and then brown as they ripen. They do considerable mechanical damage to wool and mohair. It is generally not realized that ingestion of this plant can cause death in animals. A law from as early as 1860 required farmers to eradicate this herb on pain of payment of a fine. One of the first to touch platteland farmers directly. Used medicinally in treatment of diabetes. Not grazed. Great Escarpment; Upper, Great and Little Karoo; southwestern, southern, eastern and northern Cape; Orange Free State; Natal; Transvaal; Botswana, Lesotho and Swaziland in a wide range of habitats.

178

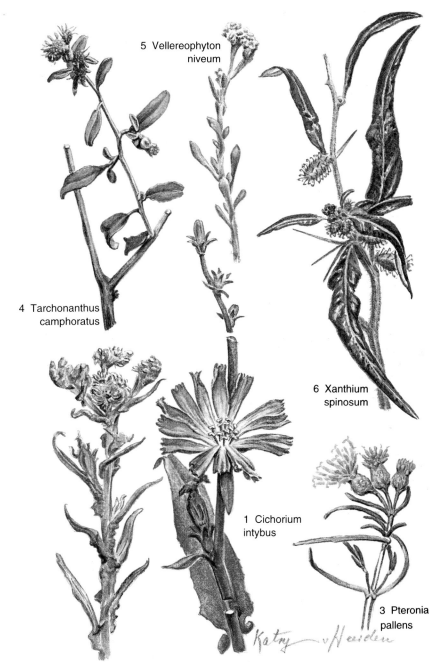

5 Vellereophyton niveum

4 Tarchonanthus camphoratus

6 Xanthium spinosum

1 Cichorium intybus

3 Pteronia pallens

2 Pseudognaphalium undulatum

INDEX